HeadStart ✓
Primary

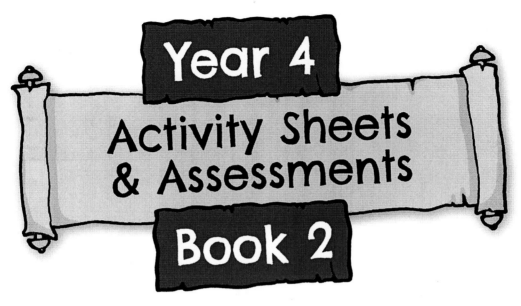

Year 4
Activity Sheets & Assessments
Book 2

Written by Clive Stack

HeadStart ✓
Primary

Acknowledgements:

Author: Clive Stack
Series Editor: Peter Sumner
Illustration and Page Design: Kathryn Webster
and Jerry Fowler

The right of Clive Stack to be identified as the author of this publication
has been asserted by him in accordance with the
Copyright, Designs and Patents Act 1998.

HeadStart Primary Ltd
Elker Lane
Clitheroe
BB7 9HZ

T. 01200 423405
E. info@headstartprimary.com
www.headstartprimary.com

Published by HeadStart Primary Ltd 2017 © **HeadStart Primary Ltd 2017**

A record for this book is available from the British Library -
ISBN: 978-1-908767-48-6

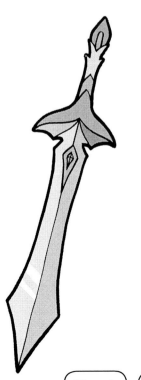

Year 4   V4

Book 2 – Contents

Teachers' Notes (i – iv)

Activity sheets

(Headings marked with the swords symbol *denote concepts not covered in Book 1.)*

Year 4

Teachers' Notes

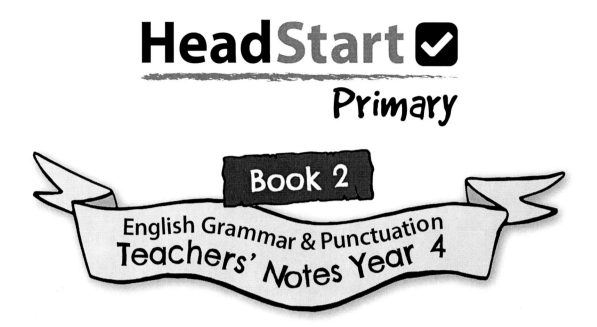

HeadStart ☑
Primary

Book 2

English Grammar & Punctuation
Teachers' Notes Year 4

Activity sheets

Book 2 contains a further set of activity sheets which follow the knight theme. They include fun facts, stories, poems, jokes and a variety of activities that will keep the children motivated and inspired. These activity sheets are designed to be used in a variety of ways at the discretion of the teacher. They may be used for whole-class sessions, group work or even as homework practice.

There are two types of additional activity sheets; those that match the objectives of Book 1, and those which introduce new concepts – some of which need to be taught in order to cover the statutory requirements for that year group. (The coverage tables at the back of this book show where the objectives have come from.) The additional activity sheets (that include objectives not covered within the main section) are clearly identified with a crossed swords symbol ✖. They are arranged in the same order as Book 1, for easy reference. However, they can be taught in whatever order the teacher feels is appropriate for the class.

End-of-Term Assessments and Optional Tests

To help the teacher assess the children's progress against the age-related expectations, there are three End-of-Term Assessments and three Optional Tests. **Raw score/scaled score conversion charts for the Optional Tests are supplied on the CD-ROM.**

The inclusion of this variety of assessment and testing options is intended to provide schools with greater flexibility, in order to meet their curriculum needs.

Year 4

Some possible approaches to testing are outlined below.

End-of-Term Assessments
The Autumn, Spring and Summer Assessments are designed to be administered at the end of each term or when the content for each section has been delivered. These assessments will only assess the children on the concepts taught for that particular term. Analysis of the results will indicate which concepts have been understood and which will require further teaching. Information gleaned from this formative approach would constitute an integral part of any assessment for learning strategy or policy.

Optional Tests
The Optional Tests feature concepts (objectives) from the whole Year 4 curriculum. Concepts from other year groups which underpin the learning for Year 4 are also included. These tests are designed to be used at any time during the school year to provide a 'snapshot' of progress against curriculum objectives. The content of each Optional Test is purposely very similar, thus enabling assessment and tracking of progress on a like-for-like basis. **Raw score/scaled score conversion charts are supplied on the CD-ROM.** Scaled scores facilitate very effective progress tracking.

One possible model is as follows:

One of the Optional Tests is administered at the very beginning of the school year as soon as the children have 'settled in'. This will provide a 'baseline' benchmark. The second Optional Test is administered halfway through the Spring Term and the third Optional Test is administered at the end of the school year to provide a summative judgement. In this way, progress can be tracked and valuable assessment data can be passed to the teacher in the next year group.

There are several other models which could be used but it is important to remember that this data should always be used to complement (and not replace) the ongoing assessment strategies and professional judgement of the teacher.

At HeadStart, we have intentionally chosen not to include too many multiple-choice questions in our assessments. Although multiple-choice questions have the advantage of being quicker and easier to mark, they do not help a teacher understand where pupils' misconceptions lie or to know when a pupil has simply guessed the correct answer. Questions that allow children to demonstrate their writing skills help teachers identify the areas where pupils are struggling and address their problems immediately.

Terminology

Terminology, which is introduced in the activity pages, is often included for the benefit of the teacher. Children need to understand the concepts, but do not always need to know the terminology until a later age group. Therefore, children will not be tested on their understanding of the terminology in the Optional Tests until the appropriate age group.

Marking and administration

The End-of-Term Assessments are marked out of 25 and it is recommended that they are completed in approximately 25 minutes. The Optional Tests are scored out of 50 and it is recommended that they are completed in approximately 50 minutes. When a tracking judgement is required, **End-of-Term** test scores should be converted to a percentage, as shown below. **Optional Test raw scores can be converted to scaled scores using the tables supplied on the CD-ROM.**

Percentage score for End-of-Term Assessment = $\dfrac{\textbf{assessment mark} \times \textbf{100}}{\textbf{25}}$ **(or score × 4)**

The table below can then be used to identify progress against one of the six stages. **(The table for the Optional Tests is supplied on the CD-ROM.)**

Percentage Score	Stage	
0 – 25	Emerging	Below average range
26 – 50	Developing	Below average range
51 – 63	Progressing	Average range
64 – 75	Secure	Average range
76 – 88	Mastering	Above average range
89 – 100	Exceeding	Above average range

0 – 50%	Below
51 – 75%	Average
76 – 100%	Above

This data should always be used in conjunction with the ongoing assessment and professional judgement of the teacher.

Answers

A complete set of answers is provided, both for the activity sheets and the tests.

Assessment and Analysis Record Sheets

Assessment/Test Record Sheet:
This sheet can be used to record pupils' scores for all the End-of-Term Assessments and the Optional Tests.

End-of-Term Assessment Analysis Grids (Autumn, Spring and Summer):
These grids can be used to record pupils' scores for the End-of-Term Assessments. The completed grids will clearly identify strengths and weaknesses.

Optional Test Analysis Grid (Tests 1, 2 and 3):
This grid can be used to record pupils' scores for the Optional Tests. The completed grid will also clearly identify strengths and weaknesses.

National Curriculum Statutory Requirements Record Sheet:
This sheet can be used to measure progress against the objectives which are National Curriculum statutory requirements. A variety of recording methods could be used on this sheet, depending on schools' or teachers' preferences.

Using the CD-ROM

The CD-ROM follows the structure of the book and contains all of the photocopiable pages, both in full colour for displaying on an interactive whiteboard and in black and white for copying or printing. It contains all the answer pages and marking schemes for the tests. **The CD-ROM also contains information and tables pertaining to scaled scores for the Optional Tests.**

Consider enlarging activity sheets to A3
to increase the space for children's writing.

Year 4

I can use capital letters, full stops and commas.

New sentences start with a capital letter. <u>He</u> always wanted to be a squire.

Proper nouns *always start with a capital letter.*
He was the squire to <u>Sir</u> Lancelot, who was one of <u>King</u> <u>A</u>rthur's knights.

Full stops *finish sentences.* He held the sword for the knight.

Commas *can go between items in a list.*
The squire carried the knight's helmet, armour, shield and sword.

Commas *can be used with a connective to join two sentences together.*

The squire liked polishing the armour, but he didn't like mucking out the horses.

Write out these sentences with the appropriate punctuation.

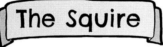

1 the young king arthur served as sir kay's squire in the story of the sword in the stone

....

....

2 squires had to develop strength speed agility and leadership skills

....

....

3 it was also his duty to learn about courtly etiquette jousting music and dancing

....

....

4 the squire not only had to serve the knight in times of peace but he also had to follow

him on to the battlefield in times of war

....

....

5 sir lancelot sir percival sir galahad and sir kay were all knights of the round table

....

....

I can use conjunctions to extend sentences.

Conjunctions *can join clauses in a compound sentence.*

Being a squire was considered a noble occupation, <u>but</u> it was also a dangerous job.

Some conjunctions can join a main clause and a subordinate clause in a complex sentence.

They remained squires <u>until</u> they had proved their ability in battle.

1 Join the beginning and end of each sentence using the correct conjunction.

 Knight Training

A noble's son could train to be a knight	and	he also needed to know how to serve at table.
He would first need to train as a page	but	being appointed a squire.
A squire would train with weapons	when	be courteous to noblewomen.
A knight would protect the weak	before	he was seven years old.

Join each pair of sentences using <u>and</u>, <u>so</u>, <u>but</u>, <u>although</u> or <u>because</u>.

2 Noblemen's sons became pages. One day they wanted to be a knight.

....

3 The squire had to teach the pages. He also had to wait on the knight.

....

4 The squire trained in swordsmanship. He could fight with the knight in battle.

....

5 The squire also had to learn about music. He needed to study the arts.

....

6 Any boy could become a squire. It helped if you came from noble birth.

....

2

Year 4

I can use full stops, question marks and exclamation marks.

We use full stops to show where sentences end.
We use question marks to show the end of a question.
We use exclamation marks for: commands, shouting, strong feelings.

Punctuate the following sentences:

Where did you put my helmet

Saddle my horse now

Would you like me to accompany you to the feast

I've been hurt

Have you cleaned my armour

I am at your service, my lady

Forward into battle

This is my young squire

What have you done with my sword

Year 4

I can use prepositions.

*Some **prepositions** tell you <u>where</u> things are in relation to other things.*

The knight was **outside** the castle walls.

*Some **prepositions** tell you <u>when</u> things happened in relation to each other.*

Knights first appeared **during** the 12th century.

❶ Colour the prepositions below.

over	in	but	however
inside	below	buried	when
under	to	if	around
because	before	through	behind

Choose a suitable preposition from the scroll below to complete each sentence.

under	to	below	over	up	inside	outside	through

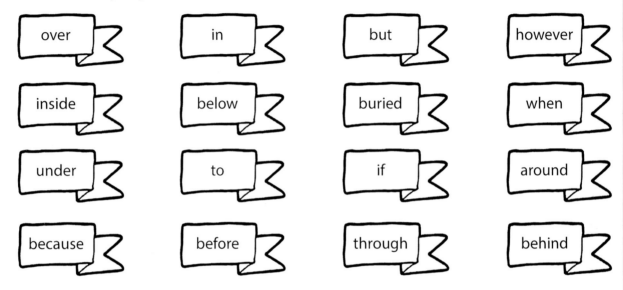

❷ The army lays siege .... the castle.

❸ The knights camp .... the castle walls.

❹ Huge mangonels hurl stones and rocks .... the battlements.

❺ The knights climb .... wooden towers called belfries.

❻ Meanwhile, miners tunnel .... the castle walls.

❼ The knights .... the castle fire arrows .... the arrow slits.

❽ Sometimes they pour burning oil on the army ....

4

I can use words to express time.

Some words or phrases can be used to tell a reader when something is happening. They place things in order of time. (The words can be conjunctions, prepositions or adverbs.)

First, invite your guests to a banquet. (Don't invite your enemies!)

Next, prepare the banqueting hall (for a minimum of a hundred guests).

Then, roast the peasants! (Sorry – that should read pheasants!)

Place the most appropriate word at the start of each sentence.

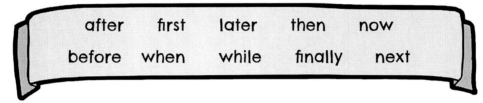

| after | first | later | then | now |
| before | when | while | finally | next |

Medieval Mealtimes

1 .... find your seat at one of the long tables.

2 .... remain standing until the king has entered.

3 .... the king has sat down, you may also sit.

4 .... you eat, wash your hands in the bowl of water when it is passed to you.

5 .... you have washed your hands, you may begin to eat.

6 .... tuck in as quickly as you can. (The food doesn't hang around for long!)

7 .... you are eating, help yourself to plenty of wine.

8 .... wipe your fingers on your sleeve. (Napkins are not provided at a medieval banquet!)

9 .... throw the bones on the floor for the dogs.

10 .... fall asleep on one of the tables with your face in a trencher!

I can use pronouns.

Pronouns replace a noun. They save you from writing the noun over and over again.
There are two types of pronouns.

This is the set you use when the person or thing is doing the action.

| I | you | he | she | it | we | they |

This is the set you use when the person or thing is having the action done to it.

| me | you | him | her | it | us | them |

*There are also **possessive pronouns** which show who owns something.*

| mine | yours | his | hers | its | ours | theirs |

Cross out incorrect pronouns in the sentences below.

The Class Assembly

At school **we / us** did an assembly about King Arthur and the Knights of the Round Table.
Miss told **we / us** that **him / he** had a round table so that the knights wouldn't fight over
who sat next to **him / he**. **They / Them** were a jealous lot back then! **I / me** took my
wooden sword into school because **me / I** was going to play the part of Sir Lancelot.
He / His was one of the most famous of the knights. My friend George was going to play
the part of King Arthur. Unfortunately, George and **I / me** fell out. My sword was bigger
than **his / its** but George said **he / him** should have the biggest one because **he / she**
was the king. When **me / I** wasn't looking George picked up my sword and began to
wave **her / it** about.

"Hey! That's **me / mine!**" I shouted. "Not **yours / ours!** Give it back to **I / me!**" and **I / me**
hit **him / his** over the head.

"Get off **me / mine!**" he shouted back. "**Me / I** hate **you / yours!**"

The children watching laughed. **Them / They** thought it was part of the play. Miss didn't
find it so amusing though and **her / she** kept **we / us** in during playtime. **We / us** weren't
given big parts to play in class assemblies ever again.

Year 4

I can identify the present and past tense of verbs.

Verb tenses *tell you when something happens. The verb changes in the different tenses.*
The present tense is used for actions that take place in the present time.
The past tense is used for actions that have already taken place.
The past tense is usually used for writing stories and historical accounts.
You can often add **ed** *to a verb to make it past tense.*
But not all verbs follow the **ed** *rule.*

Here are some examples:

is – was	are – were	can – could	go – went
take – took	have – had	grow – grew	keep – kept
give – gave	dwell – dwelt	sleep – slept	eat – ate

Life in the Middle Ages

This passage has been written in the present tense instead of the past tense. Write the past tense of the verbs above the underlined words.

The majority of people in the medieval period <u>live</u> in the country and <u>labour</u> in the fields

as farmers. They <u>grow</u> crops such as barley, wheat and oats. They sometimes <u>keep</u>

animals such as chickens, pigs and cows. They <u>give</u> most of what they <u>earn</u> to the local

lord who <u>owns</u> the land. They mostly <u>eat</u> vegetables. They <u>have</u> very hard lives.

It <u>isn't</u> much easier in the city. Most towns and cities <u>suffer</u> from overcrowding and they

<u>are</u> very dirty. Here they <u>work</u> as craftsmen and <u>belong</u> to a guild. Young boys <u>serve</u>

as apprentices for seven years learning their craft. Other jobs <u>include</u> servants,

merchants and bakers.

Some lords and their families <u>reside</u> in spacious castles, but most people <u>dwell</u> in small

one or two-room homes. The whole family often <u>sleep</u> together in the one room and

sometimes <u>share</u> the room with their animals. It <u>can</u> be very smelly! In winter they

<u>snuggle</u> up to the pigs just to stay warm!

Oink! -

I can use the present progressive and the past progressive tense.

*To show that an action is happening at the time of speaking we often use the **present progressive tense**. (Sometimes this is called the **present continuous tense**.)*
*We do this by adding an **auxiliary verb** (or **helping verb**) and an - **ing verb**.*

Look at that! The horse **is charging** down the tilting field!
Look at us! We **are learning** to joust!

*We often use the **past progressive tense** (sometimes called the **past continuous tense**) to show that a longer action in the past was interrupted by a shorter action.*

The squire **was serving** at the banquet when the king entered the hall.
While the knights **were sleeping**, the enemy attacked the castle.

Complete the sentences using the past progressive tense.

❶ The young page .... the cup with wine when he sneezed.
(to fill)

❷ The squire .... the weapons when he saw the blood on the sword.
(to clean)

❸ The squire .... to help the knight when he dismounted the horse.
(to wait)

❹ The knights ....up to the castle when the guards lowered the drawbridge.
(to ride)

❺ While the ladies ....to the music, the fool did cartwheels.
(to dance)

❻ While the guests .... and drinking, the traitor sneaked into the hall.
(to eat)

❼ When nobody .... the assassin put poison in the king's cup.
(to look)

❽ The king .... for his life as the assailant silently crept away.
(to fight)

Year 4

I can make the auxiliary verb and the main verb agree.

Auxiliary verbs are sometimes called **helping verbs** because they are needed to help form the different tenses of the main verb.
Auxiliary verbs are used in the present progressive tense.
He <u>is</u> practising his sword skills in the yard.

They are used in the past progressive tense.
He <u>was</u> practising his sword skills, but now he is mucking out the stables.

*The **to be** verb is often used as an auxiliary verb. Here is a list of the **to be** verb forms:*

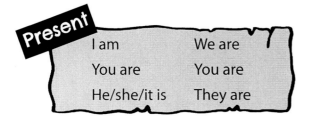

Present

I am	We are
You are	You are
He/she/it is	They are

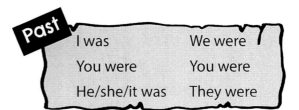

Past

I was	We were
You were	You were
He/she/it was	They were

It is quite easy to muddle the auxiliary verbs up when you are speaking. But it is really important that you correctly match the auxiliary verb with the main verb in your writing.

1 Only one of the following two sentences is correct. Tick the correct sentence.

He is sat in the stand watching the jousting. ⬚

He is sitting in the stand watching the jousting. ⬚

2 Which sentence is correct? Tick the correct one.

We were serving the lord in the Great Hall. ⬚

We was serving the lord in the Great Hall. ⬚

Place the correct auxiliary verb in the spaces provided.

3 At this very moment, the young page .... serving breakfast to the knight.
Before that he .... helping the knight to get dressed.

4 Everyone can see that the knight .... wearing his armour back-to-front.
The squire .... laughing when he realised his mistake.

5 Earlier on today, we .... preparing for the jousting tournament.
The young knight .... practising his skills on the tilting field yesterday.

6 The day before, the king .... watching the knights practising from his pavilion.
Now you .... watching the tournament from the stands.

I can use Standard English when writing verbs. ①

*In **Standard English**, the subject and the verb have to agree – they should both be singular or they should both be plural. It is easy to make mistakes when using the present progressive and the past progressive tense.*

We use the present progressive tense to show that something is happening at the moment of speaking.

He is riding his horse down the tilting field.

We often use the past progressive to show a continuous action in the past that has happened before, during or after another action.

The squire was rubbing the horse down when the knight demanded he should be saddled for the joust.

Sometimes we use the past continuous to show that something happened in the past for some length of time.

The knight's head was aching after receiving a blow to the helmet.

Cross out the incorrect option so that each sentence is in Standard English.

The Lady of the Manor

❶ The lady of the manor **was brushing / were brushing** her hair as breakfast was served.

❷ Her maids **was helping / were helping** her to get dressed for prayers in the chapel.

❸ She **were saying / was saying** her prayers in the chapel when the knight arrived.

❹ Throughout the morning, she **was sat / was sitting** in her chamber doing her needlework.

❺ Later, she **was standing / were stood** by her husband's side as he collected the rent.

❻ At supper, she ate pheasant as the musicians **were playing / was playing**.

❼ In the evening, she **were dancing / was dancing** with the young courtiers.

Year 4

I can use Standard English when writing verbs. ❷

*The present perfect uses **have** and **has** as auxiliary verbs.*

I <u>have</u> learnt to dance the galliard today. *(The galliard was a rather energetic dance!)*
He <u>has</u> learnt to play the lute this week. *(This is a string instrument, a bit like a guitar!)*

We often use the present perfect tense to show that an action has been completed recently.

I have polished your armour for you, my lord.

This means job done, but the squire has probably only just finished polishing the armour.

*Usually when we use **have** or **has** we use the normal past tense form of the verb.*

Past	**Present perfect**
I **finished** sharpening your sword.	I **have finished** sharpening your sword.

Write the present perfect tense for these sentences that are written in the simple past.

The worst jobs in the Castle

Simple Past   **Present Perfect**

❶ The doctor's assistant <u>collected</u> pond leeches. ....

❷ The chimney sweeps <u>climbed</u> the castle chimneys. ....

❸ The fullers <u>washed</u> the wool with urine. ....

❹ The squire <u>cleaned</u> the blood off the armour. ....

❺ The groom of the stool <u>carried</u> the commode. ....

❻ The gong farmers <u>emptied</u> the latrine pit. ....

❼ The cupbearer <u>tasted</u> the drink for poison. ....

❽ The barber also <u>pulled</u> out rotting teeth. ....

A commode is
like a potty!

A latrine is
like a toilet!

I can use Standard English when writing verbs. ③

*As we have seen most verbs use the **ed** form of the verb when using have or has.*
But there are some verbs that use a different past form.

Past
I **spoke** to his Lordship recently.

Present perfect
I have **spoken** to his Lordship recently.

You need to learn the ones which are different. Here are some of the most common ones:

Infinitive	Simple Past	Past Particple
be	was, were	been
break	broke	broken
come	came	come
draw	drew	drawn
drink	drank	drunk
eat	ate	eaten
go	went	gone
grow	grew	grown
know	knew	known
ride	rode	ridden
run	ran	run
see	saw	seen
sing	sang	sung
speak	spoke	spoken
take	took	taken
throw	threw	thrown
wear	wore	worn
write	wrote	written

Write the present perfect tense for these sentences which are written in the simple past.

Past   **Present Perfect**

❶ I <u>rode</u> my horse across the stream.   ....

❷ He <u>ate</u> pigeon pie for supper.   ....

❸ I <u>saw</u> the knight kiss the lady.   ....

❹ He <u>broke</u> the sword in two.   ....

❺ I <u>knew</u> the knight for years.   ....

❻ The page <u>grew</u> into a handsome knight.   ....

❼ I <u>went</u> across the drawbridge.   ....

❽ I <u>drank</u> a jug of mead.   ....

❾ The maid <u>sang</u> a sweet song.   ....

Year 4

Name:

I can use speech marks in direct speech.

Speech marks are often called inverted commas. They look like this " ..... "

Inverted commas go around the actual words that people say. They go at the start and at the end of speech.

"I will rescue the fair maiden from the dragon," said the knight.

When speech starts the sentence it will end with a comma, an exclamation mark or a question mark.

"I need my armour cleaning," said the knight.
"I'm really tired!" said the page.
"What time did you go to bed?" asked the knight.

Look at the conversation below. Write the conversation as a passage with speech.

1. It's time to get up for work, my lord.
2. Go away! It's the middle of the night!
3. I know, my lord.
4. Then what is the reason for waking me up at this unearthly hour?
5. You're on the knight shift!

....

....

....

....

....

....

I can change direct speech to reported speech.

*There are two types of speech: **direct speech** and **reported speech**.*
Direct speech is when you use the actual words that someone has said.

> **Has** anyone got a tin opener?

"**Has** anyone got a tin opener?" the knight asked.

Reported speech is when you write what someone has said in your own words.
The knight asked if anyone <u>had</u> a tin opener.
*The tense changes to the past tense (**has** changes to **had**) because you are reporting something that has already been said.*

Write these sentences as reported speech. (Hint: pronouns need to change as well.)

1 "I have come to kill the dragon," said the knight.

The knight said that he ....

2 "I do not want any more tinned food," said the dragon.

....

3 "I am the fattest knight in the kingdom," said Sir Cumference.

....

4 "I have a practical joke for the king," said Sir Prize.

....

5 "Why do you want to go to Camelot?" the mother asked her son.

....

6 "I want to go for the knight life," he replied.

....

Year 4

I can identify and use adverbs.

Adverbs describe verbs. *Adverbs of manner tell you how an action was done. They can go underline before or underline after a verb.*

The page **quickly** ran across the courtyard.
The moon shone **brightly** above the castle.

*Adverbs often end in **ly** but there are exceptions.*

That horse can gallop **fast!**

George and the Dragon

Underline the adverbs in the story below.

It was a wet and wild evening when the knight bravely rode up to the sinister-looking

inn on the outskirts of the town. The wooden sign, "George and the Dragon", creaked

noisily as it flapped back and forth in the gathering storm. He boldly went up to the

door and knocked loudly. He waited patiently for the sound of approaching footsteps,

but none came. He courageously rapped on the door again. This time a window above

suddenly crashed open and a woman's head unexpectedly emerged, her face contorted

with anger.

"What's the meaning of waking me up at this time of night?" she shrieked crossly.

"I have come to save you!" the knight heroically announced.

"Clear off!" she rudely shouted back down at him. "I don't need saving!"

"I have heard that there is someone in distress that needs rescuing," he uttered unsurely.

"There's no one in this inn needs rescuing!" she angrily replied. "Now beat it!" She shook

her fist at him threateningly. "Or I'll fetch my chamber pot!" she added ominously.

"Is there anyone else in the inn?" he asked uncertainly.

"Just me and my husband," she replied as she quickly retreated back into the room.

The knight promptly looked back at the name on the sign that was

now swinging violently to and fro in the wind.

"Can I speak to your husband George then?" he managed to

ask politely before the contents of the chamber

pot were crudely emptied all over him.

15

I can identify and use alternative verbs.

Verbs are very important because they tell you what's happening in a sentence.

In fact, if it doesn't have a verb then it's <u>not</u> a sentence!

Sometimes we can overuse the same verb. It is good to know some alternatives for frequently used verbs to make our writing more interesting.

He <u>shut</u> the castle door.   He <u>closed</u> the castle door.

<u>Closed</u> is an alternative of <u>shut</u>.

Identify the verbs in this story and replace them with alternatives. (The verbs are listed in order.)

returning	journeyed	collapsed	expired	collected	trudged
marched	rapped	bellowed	unbolted	appeared	beg
answered	departed	taken	informed	return	mount
enquired	believe	responded	conduct	spoke	escorted
vanished	emerged	guiding	staggered	stared	dispatch

What a knight!

Sir Vival, a knight of St George, was coming back from the Crusades on a cold, dark winter's night when his old, faithful horse, which had travelled many miles, fell down and died. Sir Vival gathered up what belongings he could and tramped towards a light in the distance. He strode up to the door of the inn and knocked loudly.

"A horse! A horse! I must have a horse!" he yelled. The door was unlocked and a young girl came into view.

"I ask for your pardon, good knight," she replied, "but my father and my brothers have left to go hunting in the forest and have got all the horses. They haven't told me when they will come back."

"Are there no other horses for me to ride?" he asked desperately.

"I don't think there are other horses hereabout," the girl replied, "but sometimes my brothers ride our Great Dane dog when the need arises. Would that be of any help?"

"Lead me to the animal," the knight said wearily.

In the sleet and rain the girl took the knight to the back of the inn to the stables where she disappeared inside. She came back out leading a massive dog which was quite big enough to ride. However, he was old, his coat was threadbare and he wobbled on his spindly legs.

The knight looked at the young girl disbelievingly and said, "You wouldn't send a knight out on a dog like this!"

Year 4

I can construct sentences in different ways.

*Sentences are often constructed from a **main clause** and a **subordinate clause**.
The subordinate clause can go either before, or after the main clause depending on what
needs to be emphasised.*

Just let me know **if you want more to eat**.

If you want more to eat, just let me know.

Rewrite these sentences by putting the subordinate clauses at the beginning of the sentences.

Medieval Banquets

1 There were lots of festivals to enjoy if you were rich in the medieval period.

....

2 Banquets were held often because there were so many feast days.

....

3 Musicians would play while the guests ate their food.

....

4 A jester would amuse the guests as the various courses were being served.

....

5 Acrobats, fire-eaters and conjurors entertained the guests after they had feasted.

....

6 There would be dancing when the tables were cleared.

....

7 The knights were expected to dance if the ladies requested it.

....

8 It was a lot of hard work if you were one of the servants!

....

I can identify and use paired adjectives. ❶

It is common to use more than one adjective before a noun.

When you use more than one adjective you have to put them in the right order.

It is correct to write: The page carried a **large red** flag.

But it is not correct to write: The page carried a **red large** flag.

Although there are some exceptions, the general order of adjectives in a pair is as follows:

| opinion | size | age | shape | colour | material |

So you would write:

A round metal shield.　　**A small white feather.**　　**A lazy old donkey.**

Draw a mythical monster of your own and then describe it using pairs of adjectives. Remember to put them in the right order according to type. Here is a list to get you started.

smooth　　grey　　scaly　　fat　　spotty　　old

long　　shiny　　tiny　　evil　　red

hairy　　skinny　　gentle　　young

brown　　large

short　　frightening　　sharp

black　　huge

wicked　　grumpy　　scary

wild

furry　　leathery　　pointy

round　　wrinkly　　fluffy　　white　　friendly

vicious　　puny

strong　　glowing　　enormous　　skinny　　green　　rough

Year 4

I can identify and use paired adjectives. ❷

❶ Draw your mythical monster in the box.

❷ Now describe your monster using paired adjectives.

....

....

....

....

....

....

....

....

....

I can identify a clause within a sentence.

*Sometimes **clauses** are put into a sentence to add additional detail for the reader. They do not usually make sense on their own. They are often separated from the main clause using commas.*

The horse, **which was tired and hungry**, refused to go any further.

1 Underline the clauses in the following passage.
(They begin with 'which', 'who' or 'that'.)

The Dragon Egg

Once upon a time, in a castle, which was far, far away, there was a beautiful princess. The beautiful princess, who was actually rather vain and conceited, had many admirers. One day she gazed out of her window, which was at the top of the tallest tower, to see a queue of knights. The knights, who were in their finest suits of armour, all wanted to marry her. They were patiently waiting to see the king, who was a bit of a joker, to ask for his daughter's hand in marriage. The king, who could never make his mind up, decided to send the knights out on a quest. Whichever knight could bring back an egg of a dragon, that he had vanquished in a battle, could have the hand of his daughter. (I really don't know why they wouldn't want the rest of her!)

2 Insert the most suitable clause into the sentences below.

> where the dragon had his lair
> who was a surprisingly friendly fellow
> who was called Sir Tainwyn
> which usually went everywhere with him

A young knight, ... (think about it!), had a plan to get

the dragon egg without losing his life. He rode up to the mountain, ...

.... , and requested a meeting. To demonstrate his honour

he had left his sword, ... , back at

the castle. He told the dragon, ...

.... , he would swap a dragon egg for whatever the dragon desired.

(To be continued!)

Year 4

I can use the relative pronouns 'who', 'that' and 'which'.

Relative pronouns are often used in embedded clauses.

Sometimes it can be confusing which of the three relative pronouns to use.

There are rules, but as always there are exceptions.

As a rule, who is used for people.

The princess, **who** was rescued from the dragon, was completely ungrateful.

That refers mostly to things.

The key, **that** was old and rusty, broke in the lock.

Which, like that, also refers to things.

The key, **which** the knight gave to the squire, fell through a hole in his pocket.

*For animals and pets the relative pronoun can change. If you were writing about a nameless cat that you didn't know much about you could use **that** or **which**.*

The cat, **that** had been found in the moat, chased the rats in the cellars.

The cat, **which** was a good ratter, slept in the castle kitchen.

*If the cat had a name or was a leading character in a story then you could use **who**.*

Tiger, the cat, **who** belonged to the cook, kept the rats out of the kitchen.

Insert the correct relative pronoun <u>who</u>, <u>that</u> or <u>which</u> into the following sentences.

❶ Puff the dragon, ... was a gentle creature, lived by the sea.

❷ One of the dragons, ... had been sleeping in the dormant volcano, rose up into the sky.

❸ The sword, ... had smashed against the dragon's scales, broke into a thousand pieces.

❹ The sword, ... was found buried in the sand, had magical powers.

❺ The squire, ... had slain the dragon, became a famous knight.

❻ The shield, ... had saved the knight's life, had been burnt to cinders.

❼ The horse, ... was a favourite of the knight, had gone lame.

❽ Warrior, ... was a war horse, carried knights into battle.

Year 4

21

I can recognise countable and non-countable nouns.

A **countable noun** is a thing you can count, e.g. swords.

A **non-countable noun** is something you can't count, e.g. bravery.

'My bravery will serve me well.'

The following sentence has examples of four **countable noun**s but there are also three **non-countable** nouns. Can you spot them all?

The bravery of the knight was in no doubt for as soon as he heard the weeping from the cave he charged inside to rescue the maiden, even though the dragon would soon be returning.

The **knight**, the **cave**, the **maiden**, and the **dragon** are all countable nouns.

The non-countable nouns are **bravery**, **doubt** and **weeping**.

Nouns such as stuff, money and fire are also **non-countable nouns**.

Place the following nouns in the correct box.

bravery	honesty	mountain	castle	happiness	beauty
fear	sword	strength	muscles	wound	egg
knight	sky	evil	shield	dragon	kindness

Countable	Non-countable

Year 4

Activity Sheet | Name:

I can identify and use noun phrases.

*A **noun** is a word that names the things we are talking about.*
*A **noun** names a person, a place, an animal or a thing.*
*A **noun phrase** is a phrase that tells us more information about the noun.*

The mysterious knight in black threw down his gauntlet as a challenge.
***The mysterious knight in black** is a noun phrase.*
*The words **mysterious** and **black** modify the meaning of the noun **knight**.*

The knight couldn't take his eyes away from **the princess with the bright red hair**.
***The princess with the bright red hair** is a noun phrase.*
*The words **with the bright red hair** give more information about the noun **princess**.*

Identify the noun phrases in the sentences below by underlining the phrase.

1 The warlock lived in the dark castle on the hill.

2 A grotesque creature with fang-like teeth attacked the knight.

3 The princess was locked in the tower hidden by a dense forest.

4 The lady in the blue headdress danced with all the courtiers.

5 The knight was a man of honour.

6 The young page with the shaking hands dropped the broth.

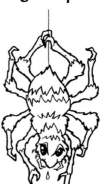

Complete the sentences by finishing the noun phrases.

7 The blacksmith with .... bent the iron bar in half.

8 The princess in .... waited to be rescued.

9 The king with .... ordered that all the prisoners should be beheaded.

10 The queen dressed in .... gave her favour to the knight.

11 Because the knight was a man of .... he could never tell a lie.

12 The dragon with .... raised its head and roared.

I can use a range of linking words or phrases.

*You can link ideas with a range of words or phrases. These can include **conjunctions**, **conjunctive adverbs** and **adverbials**.*

Sometimes you will find them in a middle of a sentence.

The knight enjoyed sword fighting, **but** he hated jousting.

Sometimes you will find them at the beginning of a sentence.

The knight enjoyed sword fighting. **On the other hand**, he hated jousting.

Underline the most suitable words or phrases in the passage below.

The brothers Triston and Raymond were both squires, **(although / because)** their lives couldn't have been more different. **(On the one hand / Even though)**, they were close in age and looked very similar. **(Furthermore / On the other hand)**, they had very different personalities. Triston was hard working, obedient and responsible, **(if / but)** Raymond was lazy, argumentative and was always up to mischief. **(While / Yet)**, despite all his shortcomings, Raymond had an excellent sense of humour, which would prove useful in the end.

(Even though / Whenever) sword fighting was dangerous and tiring, Triston would practise his skills all day long **(until / unless)** he got them right. **(In contrast / Whenever)**, Raymond would soon give up and would run off to the stables to practise his juggling.

(While / Although) Triston was up early in the morning preparing the knight's breakfast, Raymond would be fast asleep in bed. **(Because / Although)** Triston was so determined and conscientious he was quickly made into a knight. **(However / Although)**, Raymond was just not cut out for the responsibility. **(Consequently / However)**, Triston became a brave and dashing knight, **(since / whereas)** Raymond decided his talents lay elsewhere and he became the court jester.

24

I can use a range of prepositions.

Prepositions tell you how things are related to one another.
Prepositions of place tell you where things are in relation to other things in the sentence.
The squire was found hiding **under** the bed.
The knight had to ride **on** Blaze the pony.

1 Underline the prepositions in the following sentences.

The court jester or fool could be found at court entertaining the king and queen.

He would wear brightly coloured clothes and a hat with bells upon it.

Queen Elizabeth I had a fool that often sat by her side.

Some would sing and play musical instruments. Others could juggle and walk on stilts.

As well as making jokes, they would often say things that came into their heads.

Henry VIII's fool would often give bad news to him, which no one else would dare.

2 Write the appropriate preposition in the box to show where the balls have landed..

| between | under | beside | in front of | behind | inside | on top of | through |

© Copyright HeadStart Primary Ltd

I can change statements into questions.

Statements tell us about something.

Questions always ask about something.

Questions often start with a question word: **who**, **what**, **when**, **where**, **why**, **which** and **how**.

But sometimes statements can be rearranged to make questions.

There **will** be feasting in the castle.   **Will** there be feasting in the castle?

The auxiliary verb (will) goes at the beginning of the sentence to form a question.

If there is no auxiliary verb then it can be changed into a question using **do**, **does** *or* **did** *as the first word.*

The jester makes jokes.   Does the jester make jokes?

(After **do**, **does** *or* **did** *we use the first form of the verb: e.g. make, not makes.)*

Make these statements into questions.

1 The jester juggles his balls.

....

2 He can also play the lute.

....

3 Henry VIII's jester was called Will Sommer.

....

4 Shakespeare wrote about fools in his plays.

....

5 Jesters were popular in Ancient Egypt as well as Medieval England.

....

6 The joker or jester can be seen in a pack of playing cards.

....

Year 4

I can use fronted adverbials.

*Adverbs describe verbs. They can come **before** or **after** the verb they are describing.*

The page **patiently** waited for the knight to finish drinking.

The page waited **patiently** for the knight to finish drinking.

Sometimes the adverb can go at the start of the sentence.
*These are called **fronted adverbials**.*

Patiently, the page waited for the knight to finish drinking.

We use a comma after the fronted adverbial.

Rearrange the sentences so that they start with a fronted adverbial.

The troubadour sang sweetly to the beautiful music.

....

The lady elegantly danced the quadrille all through the evening.

....

The jester energetically danced the jig to entertain the guests.

....

The musicians played enthusiastically during the banquet.

....

The serving girl carelessly spilt the wine over the king.

....

The king furiously shouted at her and demanded that she leave.

....

She timidly cleaned up the mess and left crying.

....

I can use fronted adverbial phrases.

Just like an adverb, an adverbial phrase adds more detail or further information to a <u>verb</u>. They act just like adverbs, but are made up of more than one word.

The page <u>ran</u> for the wine **as fast as he could**.
The squire <u>waited</u> for the knight **by the watchtower**.
The lady of the manor <u>danced</u> **all night long**.

*The adverbial phrases in bold explain **how**, **where** or **when** something happened.*
Just like adverbs they can be placed at the front of a sentence.
A comma is normally used after the adverbial phrase.

As fast as he could, the page ran for the wine.
By the watchtower, the squire waited for the knight.
All night long, the lady of the manor danced.

Identify the adverbial phrases in these sentences and place them at the start of the sentence to make fronted adverbial phrases. (Don't forget the comma.)

1 He slipped across the drawbridge quickly and quietly.

....

2 The dark tower loomed in front of them silent and forbidding.

....

3 The knight reached the castle before sunset.

....

4 He polished the armour as fast as he could.

....

5 He found a bloodstained banner outside the city walls.

....

6 You need to wear a fur cloak in the depth of winter.

....

7 The castle was attacked in the middle of the night.

....

Year 4

Name:

I can identify and use adverbs that do not end in 'ly'.

*Confusingly, not all <u>adverbs</u> end in **ly**.*

***Late**, **hard**, **fast** and **always** are examples of <u>adverbs</u> that do not end in **ly**.*

*Then there are some <u>adjectives</u> that do end in **ly**.*

***Elderly**, **friendly**, **lovely** and **ugly** are examples of <u>adjectives</u> that end in **ly**.*

**Identify and underline the adverbs in these sentences.
(Tip: first find the verbs!)**

Crime and Punishment

1 People were punished hard for committing crimes in medieval times.

2 The accused didn't spend long in gaol.

3 They went straight to court and trial by jury.

4 For minor crimes, people were often placed in the stocks.

5 For more serious crimes, people would always end up losing a body part.

6 For very serious crimes, they would almost certainly end up losing their head.

7 The executioner had to strike the neck well.

8 Executioners often took several blows before the head was removed from the body.

9 Anne Boleyn decided she would rather die by the sword than the axe.

10 I imagine she slept little the night before her execution!

Year 4

I can identify different word classes.

*We have looked at the eight different **word classes** (parts of speech): **articles** (including the **definite** and the **indefinite article**), **nouns** (including **proper nouns**, **common nouns**, **abstract nouns**), **pronouns**, **verbs** (including **auxiliary verbs**), **adjectives**, **adverbs**, **prepositions** and **conjunctions**.*

See if you can correctly identify the different word classes by labelling the underlined words.

1 Castles were first built by the <u>Normans</u> in the 11th century. ....

2 There are still lots of <u>castles</u> all over Britain that you can visit. ....

3 The Normans <u>built</u> castles to help them defend the land that they had conquered. ....

4 They were <u>often</u> built on hills so the enemy could be seen from far away. ....

5 Castles were often <u>damp</u> and draughty in the winter. ....

6 The main building was called the keep, <u>which</u> was protected by walls and towers. ....

7 Often there was a deep ditch dug <u>around</u> the castle called the moat. ....

8 Prisoners <u>were</u> kept in the basements called the dungeons. ....

9 Toilets, called garderobes, were built along the inside of <u>the</u> castle walls. ....

10 <u>Everything</u> from the toilet dropped down into the castle moat. ....

11 Lots of people were needed to keep the castle running <u>smoothly</u>. ....

12 It wasn't easy to attack a castle, <u>but</u> people tried anyway. ....

13 <u>They</u> used siege towers, battering rams and trebuchets to attack the castle. ....

14 <u>Victory</u> for the attacking side was rare. ....

Year 4

Name:

I can identify and use alternative words.

*Some words mean **the same** or have a **very similar meaning** to another word.*

So if we have a word for something why do we need another word for the same thing?

There are several reasons. Sometimes we need to repeat what we've said and we don't want to keep using the same word. In order to make our language more interesting we should try to vary the words we use.

Use a thesaurus to find alternatives for the underlined words in the sentences.

1 Dragons are among the world's most popular mythical <u>creatures</u>. ....

2 They have a long and <u>interesting</u> history. ....

3 No one is quite sure when stories of dragons first <u>appeared</u>. ....

4 But in all stories from the Greeks to the early Christians they were described as <u>huge</u>, flying serpents. ....

5 In some cultures they were useful and protective, but by medieval times they were nearly always described as harmful and <u>dangerous</u>. ....

6 When people in the past unearthed large bones, they <u>mistook</u> what we now know to be dinosaur bones for the bones of dragons. ....

7 Most people can <u>imagine</u> a dragon clearly in their heads. ....

8 They are very popular in books and <u>films</u> from "How to Train Your Dragon" through to "The Hobbit". ....

9 They typically <u>protect</u> hoards of treasure such as mountains of gold. ....

10 They nearly all breathe fire and can <u>fly</u> into the sky with gigantic wings. ....

I can identify and use the present perfect and the past perfect tense.

*Both the **present perfect** and the **past perfect** talk about something that happened before a particular point in time.*

*They are formed by using **has**, **have** or **had** with the past participle.*

*We use the **present perfect** for an action that started in the past and continues into the present.*

"I **have** reigned as your monarch for six months," said the king.

Sometimes we use it for an action that happened before an unspecified time.

"I **have fought** in battle twice," said the knight.

*We use the **past perfect** for an action that happened before a time in the past.*

Before the knight fought the dragon, **he had** eaten three Shredded Wheat for breakfast.

Choose the correct form of the verb to complete the sentences.

1 When the king cut into the pie, he discovered that the cook .... four and twenty blackbirds inside it. *(had hidden / has hidden)*

2 The maid said a blackbird .... off her nose when she was hanging out the clothes. *(has pecked / had pecked)*

3 The young page .... how to read. *(had learnt / has learnt.)*

4 By the end of the evening, the queen .... with all the Knights of the Round Table. *(has danced / had danced)*

5 "I .... you to Sir Galahad," said the lady-in-waiting. *(haven't introduced / hadn't introduced)*

6 "I .... a fair maiden," admitted the knight. *(have never rescued / had never rescued)*

7 When the queen opened the pantry door, she realised that the knave of hearts .... the tarts. *(had stolen / has stolen)*

8 The knave was arrested but he swore he ....the tarts. *(hasn't taken / hadn't taken)*

9 The squire .... the art of sword fighting yet. *(hasn't mastered / hadn't mastered.)*

32

Year 4

I can tell the difference between a coordinating conjunction and a subordinating conjunction.

*A **coordinating conjunction** is used to join two parts of a sentence as an equal pair. ('**And**', '**but**', '**so**', '**or**' and '**yet**' are **coordinating conjunctions**.)*

*A **subordinating conjunction** is used to join two parts of a sentence that have an unequal relationship. ('**Although**', '**until**', '**when**', '**if**', '**while**', '**because**' and '**before**' are **subordinating conjunctions**.)*

Circle the type of <u>conjunction</u> used in the sentences below.

1 Although he searched everywhere, the gaoler could not find the keys to the gaol.

coordinating / subordinating

2 The king told the fool to stop his jests and everyone agreed.

coordinating / subordinating

3 His arm was badly broken when he fought the Black Knight.

coordinating / subordinating

4 The court physician dressed his wounds, yet it wasn't enough to save his life.

coordinating / subordinating

5 The prince climbed to the top of the tower so he could rescue the princess.

coordinating / subordinating

6 While the music played, the page sneaked in through a side door.

coordinating / subordinating

7 The king went hunting, but the queen decided to stay at home.

coordinating / subordinating

8 They lit the fires in the castle because it was very cold.

coordinating / subordinating

I can use a range of prefixes.

Prefixes *go at the beginning of a word.*
They change the meaning of a word.
Prefixes can often give the root word the opposite meaning.
Prefixes that give words the opposite meaning are:

dis-   im-   in-   un-   ir-

Write the root word to complete the words in these sentences.

| possible   happy   regular   visible   appear |

1 The warlock used magic to <u>dis</u> .... into a cloud of smoke.

2 The knight found it <u>im</u> .... to get close to the fire-breathing dragon.

3 He was able to hide using his magic <u>in</u> .... cloak.

4 The princess was very <u>un</u> .... to be locked in the tower.

5 The shield was an <u>ir</u> .... shape after the dragon damaged it.

Other common prefixes are:

re- *usually means* **again**   **trans-** *can mean* **across**, **beyond** *or* **change**

| rebuild   transform   reheat   transport   recover   transfix |

6 Write some sentences of your own using the words above.

....

....

....

....

....

....

34

Year 4

Name:

I can use the apostrophe for contractions.

Apostrophes join two words together.
The apostrophe shows where you have missed out letters. When you make a new word by joining two words together it is called a contraction.

Some common contractions (There are too many to list them all here!):

I'm I am	*I'll* I will	*I'd* I would	*I've* I have	*I'd* I had
he's he is	*he'll* he will	*he'd* he would	*he's* he has	*he'd* he had

Some common contractions negating a verb:

isn't is not	**wasn't** was not	**hasn't** has not	**hadn't** had not	**don't** do not	**doesn't** does not

Some contractions are a bit different:
won't doesn't quite fit the missing letters from **will not**

can't is a shorter version of just one word **cannot**

Rewrite the underlined words using the apostrophe for contraction.

I <u>have not</u> been so humiliated in all my life! <u>I have</u> been outside this castle all night in the rain. I shouted to the guard, but I <u>could not</u> make myself heard and he <u>did not</u> let down the drawbridge. <u>It has</u> rained non-stop and now <u>I am</u> chilled to the bone. I <u>do not</u> care that <u>I am</u> supposed to be rescuing the princess from the dragon. <u>I will</u> not be fighting any dragons today. In fact I <u>will not</u> be fighting any dragons ever again if you <u>do not</u> help me soon. <u>Where is</u> my squire? <u>He is</u> going to be for it when I get my hands on him! <u>I had</u> told him quite clearly my suit of armour needed oiling, but he <u>was not</u> listening. He <u>could not</u> have cared less. Now the rain has rusted the armour and I <u>cannot</u> move! Somebody fetch a tin opener!

....

....

....

....

....

....

....

....

Year 4

35

I can use regular and irregular plurals.

*Most nouns form their plural by adding either **s** (books, castles, dragons) or **es** (boxes, crosses, witches). These are called **regular plurals**.*

*But not all nouns follow the same pattern. In fact, some of our most common nouns have an **irregular plural** form (child / child**ren**, woman / wom**en**).*

Here is a list of nouns:

dwarf	goose	tower	loaf	man	city
mouse	ox	church	tooth	branch	wizard
thief	wife	foot	child	person	louse

Here is a list of their plural forms:

geese	mice	thieves	men	oxen	towers
churches	people	loaves	cities	wizards	feet
teeth	lice	dwarves	wives	branches	children

Match the singular noun with their plural form and write them in the correct shield.

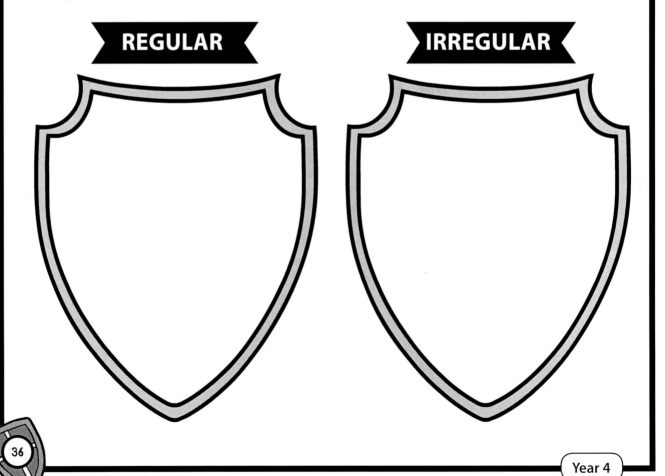

REGULAR

IRREGULAR

Year 4

I can identify the different parts of a sentence.

*The **subject** of a sentence is a **noun** that <u>performs</u> the action.*

*The **object** of a sentence is a **noun** that <u>receives</u> the action.*

The **knight** fought the dragon. (subject) The knight fought the **dragon**. (object)

*A **pronoun** (he, she it) can also serve as a subject or an object in a sentence.*

He fought the dragon. (subject) The knight fought **it**. (object)

In other words the subject is the person or thing doing something, and the object is the person or thing having something done to them.

State whether the underlined words are the subject or the object of the sentence.

The Legend of Arthur

<u>Arthur</u> was the first born son of King Uther Pendragon. ....

<u>He</u> was heir to the throne. ....

Merlin was worried about the <u>safety</u> of the young prince. ....

He took the <u>baby</u> to a safe place where he was raised in secret. ....

When King Uther died, <u>nobody</u> could agree who would be the next king. ....

<u>Merlin</u> used his magic to set a sword into the stone. ....

He wrote on the <u>stone</u> in letters of gold. ....

"<u>Whoso</u> pulleth out this sword of this stone is the rightwise born king of all England." ....

Nobles came from far and wide to try to pull the <u>sword</u> from the stone. ....

Not even the strongest men could do <u>it</u>. ....

When Arthur was fifteen, <u>Merlin</u> took him to a tournament. ....

<u>Sir Kay</u> had lost his sword. ....

Arthur went to fetch <u>him</u> one. ....

Arthur saw the <u>sword</u> in the stone and pulled it out. ....

The crowd cheered for <u>Arthur</u> when he was crowned king. ....

I can use the apostrophe for possession.

We have seen how apostrophes can be used for contraction. They can also be used to show that something belongs to someone or something. These apostrophes are called **apostrophes of possession**.

To show possession you add an **apostrophe** *and an* **s** *to the owner.*

The <u>squire's</u> sword was made from wood.

Even if the word ends in an **s** *you still do the same.*

Sir <u>Charles's</u> sword was forged from silver.

If something belongs to a group of people and the plural ends in **s** *then just add an apostrophe.*

The soldiers' helmets were made from steel.

If it is an irregular plural and doesn't end in **s** *then add an* **apostrophe** *and an* **s**.

<u>Women's</u> clothes were made of wool and linen.

Rewrite each phrase using the possessive form of the noun. The first one has been done for you.

1 the hammer of the blacksmith   the blacksmith's hammer ....

2 the keys of the bailiff   ....

3 the brushes of the grooms   ....

4 the headdresses of the ladies   ....

5 the washing tub of the laundress   ....

6 the birds of prey of the falconer   ....

7 the hats of the pages   ....

8 the swords of the knights   ....

9 the quills of the scribe   ....

10 the spears of the guardsmen   ....

Year 4

I can use the apostrophe correctly. ①

Apostrophes used incorrectly are one of the most common punctuation mistakes.

There are two reasons to use the apostrophe.

1. *For contractions.*
2. *For possession.*

*Don't get apostrophe happy and use it every time you write a plural or see an **s** at the end of a word.*

Example: The knight's ride the horse's into battle.

Does this make sense if this was a contraction? **The <u>knight is</u> ride the <u>horse is</u> into battle.** *NO!*

*Does **ride** belong to the knight or **into** belong to the horse? NO! So it's not used for possession either.*

Decide which words need apostrophes and which don't, and correct them accordingly.

Merlin

❶ There are many magical legend's about Merlin the magician.

❷ Its thought he came from a town in Wales' called Caer Myrddin, which means Merlins town.

❸ He worked for four different king's including King Uther.

❹ But he's best known as King Arthurs adviser.

❺ However, Merlin had many adventure's before working for King Arthur.

❻ There are many stories' about King Arthur and Merlin.

❼ Merlin was responsible for Arthurs education when he was a boy.

❽ If it wasnt for Merlins scheming, the crown wouldnt have been put on Arthurs head.

❾ There are several version's of Merlin's death.

❿ The most famous' one is where the Lady of the Lake use's Merlins own magic to entomb him in a rock.

I can use the apostrophe correctly. ❷

*The words **it's** and **its** confuse people all the time.*

*We only use **it's** with an apostrophe when it is a contraction.*

It's a beautiful day to go riding   (**It is** a beautiful day to go riding.)

***Its** (without an apostrophe) means something belonging to it. It shows possession.*

The horse needs new horseshoes: **its** hooves are badly worn.

---

*The words **your** and **you're** also confuse people.*

***Your** is the possessive form of you.*

Your pony has been groomed by the stable boy.

***You're** is the contraction of you are.*

You're enjoying your ride through the countryside.

These sentences have not been punctuated correctly using the apostrophe. Write out each sentence correctly.

The Blacksmith's Assistant

❶ Your working for the blacksmith. ....

❷ Its an important job at the castle. ....

❸ You're furnace needs more heat. ....

❹ Your using the bellows. ....

❺ Your'e leading in a horse. ....

❻ It's shoe needs mending. ....

❼ Its' armour is damaged. ....

❽ Its a hard job repairing a horses armour. ....

I can use regular and irregular adjectives to compare (Standard English). ①

*Adjectives can be used to compare **two** things.*
They can tell you if something is bigger, better or faster than another thing.

*They can also tell you if something is the biggest, best or fastest within a **group** of things.*

---

*Most adjectives to compare two things are formed by adding **er**, but there are exceptions to the rule.*

*Words of two syllables not ending in **y** need the word **more** inserted before the adjective.*
*The young prince is **more** charming than his older brother.*

*Words of three syllables or more also need the word **more** inserted before the adjective.*
*The young princess wore a **more** beautiful dress than her older sister.*

---

*Most adjectives to compare three or more things are formed by adding **est**, but the same rules apply as for adjectives to compare two things.*

*If the word is two syllables and does not end in **y** then insert **most** before the adjective. The young prince is the **most** charming prince in the kingdom.*

*If the word is three syllables or more then insert **most** before the adjective. The young princess wore the **most** beautiful dress at the ball.*

---

*However, there are some adjectives where either **er** or **more** is used to compare two things.*
*There are some adjectives where either **est** or **most** is used to compare three or more things.*

What would you use?

	Comparing two things	**Comparing three or more things**
❶ clever	....	....
❷ gentle	....	....
❸ narrow	....	....
❹ polite	....	....
❺ quiet	....	....
❻ simple	....	....
❼ friendly	....	....
❽ handsome	....	....

I can use regular and irregular adjectives to compare (Standard English). ②

Falconry

Falconry was a very popular sport in medieval times as well as now.

Peregrine Falcon

Fact File
Length: 15-21 inches
Wingspan: 42 inches
Weight: 2 lbs
Lifespan: 7-15 years
Speed: 200 mph
Clutch size: 3-4 eggs
Population: 1,400 pairs

Harris Hawk

Fact File
Length: 22 inches
Wingspan: 48 inches
Weight: 2½ lbs
Lifespan: 13-20 years
Speed: 150 mph
Clutch size: 2-4 eggs
Population: 430 pairs

Common Kestrel

Fact File
Length: 13-15 inches
Wingspan: 27-31 inches
Weight: ½ lb
Lifespan: 10 years
Speed: 100 mph
Clutch size: 3-6 eggs
Population: 38,600 pairs

Using your knowledge of adjectives to compare, write sentences about the various birds of prey that were used for falconry.

Adjectives you may want to use could include:

long   short   heavy   light   fast   slow   big   small   common   rare

....
....
....
....
....
....
....
....

42

I can use paragraphs to organise ideas. ①

Paragraphs break up chunks of text. We start a new paragraph on a new line.

We start new paragraphs in story writing (fiction) when:
- *There is a change of place*
- *There is a change of time*
- *There is a change of speaker*
- *There is a change of character*

We start new paragraphs in non-fiction when:
- *There is a new piece of information*
- *There is a new point of view*

Read this letter from Lucius Stone to Lord Balderdash and mark where new paragraphs should begin with //. (Clue: there should be four paragraphs.)

Fortress Hemlock
The Land Beyond the Wall,
Somewhere Up North.

Dear Lord Balderdash,

Please excuse my omissions and absent-mindedness in my previous correspondence. It was ridiculous of me to expect you to answer my ransom when I failed to give you my contact details. However, I have now put this matter right. So down to business! I believe I made a small request for your title and lands in exchange for your daughter. I have now reconsidered this and I believe I was being far too generous. As well as your castle, I think it's only fair you hand over all your worldly goods. (You can keep your wife!) Please find enclosed a lock of your daughter's hair. Apart from this lock of hair she is still in one piece (for the time being!). However, I find her incredibly irritating and I'm not sure how long my patience will last. Send a knight with your answer and a pot of gold as a gesture of goodwill. You have forty-eight hours to reply. By the way, the two fools you sent to rescue her are now locked up in the tower as well.

Kind regards,
Lucius Stone (Evil Warlock)

xxx

P.S. Ignore the kisses.

I can use paragraphs to organise ideas. 2

Indicate where the paragraphs should begin with //.

The Dragon Egg

The continued story from page 19. (If you can remember that far back!)

Once upon a time there was a beautiful princess. This beautiful princess, who was rather vain and conceited, had many admirers. One day she gazed out of her window to see a long queue of knights who were all eager to marry her. They were patiently waiting to see the king to ask him for his daughter's hand in marriage. The king, who liked playing pranks, decided to send the knights out on a quest. Whichever knight could bring back the egg of a dragon first could have the hand of his daughter. (I really don't know why they wouldn't want the rest of her!) Many knights attempted the daring feat, but all returned fried (terri-fried!). A young knight, who was called Sir Tainwyn (think about it!), had a plan to get the dragon egg without turning into a burnt crisp. He rode up to the mountain, where the dragon had his lair, to request a meeting. First, he had to wake the dragon who (because of the nature of his work) had to sleep during the day. At first, the dragon wasn't best pleased to be woken up, but when he saw that the knight was unarmed, he welcomed him into his cave for a chat. The knight told him about his plan to swap a dragon egg for whatever the dragon desired. The dragon, who was a surprisingly friendly and amenable fellow, listened carefully and then informed him that, being a boy dragon, he didn't lay eggs and therefore couldn't help him with his request. However, he was a very practical dragon and he had a suggestion that would benefit them both. Later that day, the knight rode back to the castle with a package under his arms, and announced that he had returned with dragon eggs. The whole court assembled in the throne room to watch him undo the package. He unwrapped an egg no bigger than a chicken's egg and, placing a string around it, pulled it across the floor to where the king was sitting. The king, perplexed, asked what he was doing for it was clearly not big enough to be a dragon egg. The knight replied, "Can you not see what I am doing? I'm dragon eggs behind me!" The king, who was a bit of a joker himself (I think I mentioned this), loved the practical joke and proclaimed the knight the winner. Sir Tainwyn married the princess shortly afterwards, though sadly it wasn't a happy marriage. The dragon benefitted the most from the arrangement that they had made. What was his reward? He didn't have to work knight shifts ever again!

I can generate word families based on root words.

*A **word family** is a set of words with the same **root**.*
*A **root word** is a word that can have **prefixes** and **suffixes** added to it.*
*A **prefix** is a group of letters added to the beginning of a word.*
*A **suffix** is a group of letters added to the end of a word.*
*For example: **friend**, friendly, unfriendly, friendless, befriend*

Pick at least one prefix or suffix to add to each root word to make a new word.

Prefix	Root	Suffix	New Words	
im	**port**	ation	....	....
re	**believe**	ed	....	....
mis	**danger**	ful	....	....
dis	**differ**	ly	....	....
un	**appear**	able	....	....
en	**possible**	ance	....	....
	fair	ment	....	....
	excite	ence	....	....
	thank	ant	....	....
	spell	ent	....	....
	view	ous	....	....
	imagine	less	....	....

"I'm on a quest for new words!"

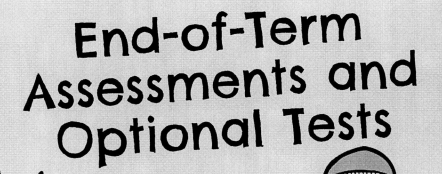

End-of-Term Assessments and Optional Tests

Raw score/scaled score conversion charts for the Optional Tests are supplied on the CD-ROM.

Year 4 Grammar & Punctuation

Autumn Assessment

Name .... Class .... Date ....

1 Rewrite this sentence and put in any missing **full stops**, **capital letters** and **commas**.

we practise netball on tuesday wednesday and thursday

....

2 marks

2 Add a **full stop**, **question mark** or **exclamation mark** at the end of these sentences.

Call an ambulance ☐

Did you hand out the newsletters ☐

I took the register to the office ☐

2 marks

3 Underline the **conjunctions** in each of these sentences.

He used to be a professional footballer until he injured his knee.

She used to have lots of friends before she moved to the new school.

2 marks

4 Circle the **preposition** in the list below.

it   mine   through   because   grammar

1 mark

1

Page Total

Year 4 Grammar & Punctuation

Autumn Assessment

5 Choose words to show that the order of the sentences below is correct. You can use a combination of **conjunctions**, **prepositions** and **adverbs** to express time. (The first one has been done for you.)

...... **First** ...... he put the tea bag in the mug and boiled the water.

.... he poured the boiling water in the mug.

.... the tea had brewed he took out the tea bag.

.... he added milk and sugar to taste.

2 marks

6 Use the **possessive pronouns** in the box to complete the sentences below.

yours	mine	theirs

Arthur took my pen even though he knew it was.....................................

Zoe and Ayesha said that the cat was.....................................

I found this scarf on the playground. I think it is ....

1 mark

7 The sentences below are written in the **present tense**. Write the **past tense** of the **verbs** on the dotted lines.

I give chocolates to my mum on her birthday.

....

We sleep in our caravan.

....

2 marks

2

Year 4 Grammar & Punctuation

Autumn Assessment

8 Circle the correct form of the **verb**, so that it is written in **Standard English**.

She **was standing / were standing** outside the gate when the school bell rang.

They **was practising / were practising** for their class assembly all morning.

2 marks

9 Correct the following sentences so that they are written in **Standard English**.

I done all my homework.

....

I have wrote it twice.

....

2 marks

10 Put **speech marks** in the sentences below.

Where have you been? asked Mum.

I have been worried, she added.

2 marks

11 Rewrite the following, putting the speech at the end of the sentence.

"I have seen United play twice," said Naeem.

....

1 mark

12 Put a circle around the **adverbs** in these sentences.

The tortoise made its way slowly to the finishing line.

Sit down quickly and open your books.

She shouted angrily at the misbehaving children.

1 mark

Page Total

Year 4 Grammar & Punctuation

Autumn Assessment

13 Place the two most appropriate **conjunctions** from the box in the sentences below.

before	although	until	so

I won't play on the PlayStation .... I have finished my spelling homework.

Tahir hurt my feelings .... he didn't mean to.

2 marks

14 Replace the underlined **proper nouns** in the sentence below with appropriate **pronouns**. (The proper nouns have been underlined for you.)

<u>Hana</u> hid <u>Henry's</u> mobile phone in <u>Hana's</u> coat pocket.

....

2 marks

15 Complete the sentence using a verb of your own in the **past progressive tense**.

I .... my book when you called.

1 mark

End of Autumn Assessment

Page Total

TOTAL

/ 25

PERCENTAGE SCORE

%

4

Year 4 Grammar & Punctuation

Spring Assessment

Name .... Class .... Date ....

1 Rewrite this sentence and put in any missing **full stops**, **capital letters** and **commas**.

ben joe and sam are running

....

2 marks

2 Draw a line matching the **verb** to another **verb** with a similar meaning.
(The first one has been done for you.)

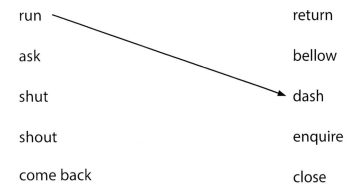

run	return
ask	bellow
shut	dash
shout	enquire
come back	close

2 marks

3 Change the structure of the sentence below so that it starts with the underlined **conjunction**.

I laughed <u>when</u> she told a joke.

....

2 marks

4 Use **two adjectives** of your own to describe the nouns in each of these sentences.

The .... man struggled to get out of his chair.

He crawled unseen through the .... grass.

2 marks

1

Page Total

Year 4 Grammar & Punctuation

5 Complete the sentences below with **subordinate clauses** of your own, using different **subordinating conjunctions**.

The teacher awarded the boy a certificate ....

....

The old lady hurt her leg ....

....

2 marks

6 Circle the noun below which is a **non-countable noun**.

table   pencil   bravery   February

1 mark

7 Choose the most appropriate **conjunctions** from the box below to complete the sentences.

before	so	although	while

Max pretended that he was in Year Three .... that he would get into dinner first.

Mrs Jones managed to mark the books .... the children were quietly working.

2 marks

8 Complete the sentences by writing your own **prepositions** in the spaces.

Megan dropped the calculator .... the table when she saw the teacher coming.

Charlie hid the answers to the tables test .... two pieces of paper.

2 marks

2

Page Total

Year 4 Grammar & Punctuation

Spring Assessment

9 Write the following statement as a **question**.

You are going swimming.

....

1 mark

10 Write out the sentences putting the **adverb** at the beginning of the sentence.

Fiona happily skipped across the bridge.

....

Kayleigh carelessly spilt her drink.

....

2 marks

11 Put the **adverbial phrase** at the beginning of the sentence.

Kian read the book as quickly as he could.

....

2 marks

12 Underline the **adverbs** in these sentences.

George can run fast.

The teacher praises us often.

Tanya always ends up in trouble even when it isn't her fault.

1 mark

3

Page Total

Year 4 Grammar & Punctuation

Spring Assessment

13 Complete the sentences below with an appropriate **subordinate clause**.

Sienna liked the teacher who ....

....

Imran picked up the pencils which ....

....

2 marks

14 Underline the **noun phrases** in these sentences.

The derelict house with the broken windows looked very scary.

The boy in the striped red shirt was very loud.

2 marks

End of Spring Assessment

 Page Total

TOTAL

/ 25

PERCENTAGE SCORE

%

4

Year 4 Grammar & Punctuation

Summer Assessment

Name .... Class .... Date ....

1 Identify the different **word classes** (parts of speech) by putting the following words under the correct headings.

window	sadly	above	walked	because	she	massive

noun	verb	adjective	adverb
....	....	....	....

preposition	pronoun	conjunction
....	....	....

2 marks

2 Draw a line matching the **adjectives** to another **adjective** with a similar meaning. (The first one has been done for you.)

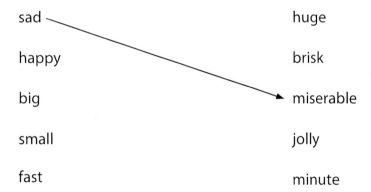

sad	huge
happy	brisk
big	miserable
small	jolly
fast	minute

2 marks

3 Circle the correct form of the **present perfect tense** to complete the sentence.

I **have thought / have thinked** about nothing else.

1 mark

Page Total

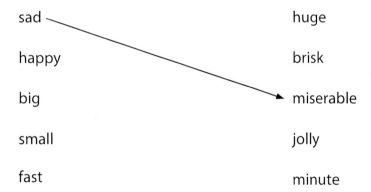

1

Year 4 Grammar & Punctuation

Summer Assessment

4 Are the underlined clauses **coordinating clauses** or **subordinating clauses**? Circle the correct option.

She couldn't find her purse <u>although she had looked everywhere</u>.

coordinating / subordinate

Tom leapt up from his chair, <u>and ran out of the classroom</u>.

coordinating / subordinate

2 marks

5 Circle the correct **prefix** for each of the words below.

un / **dis** happy   **im** / **un** possible   **dis** / **un** agree

2 marks

6 Show you can use the **apostrophe for contraction** by writing the shorter version of these words.

do not ....   I have ....   he will ....

2 marks

7 Write the **irregular plural** of these nouns.

foot ....   child ....   mouse ....

1 mark

8 Underline the **subordinate clauses** in the following sentences.

Sam is drinking a glass of water because she is thirsty.

The children go into school when the bell rings.

2 marks

2

Page Total

Year 4 Grammar & Punctuation

Summer Assessment

9 Rewrite the following phrases using the **apostrophe for possession**.

The pen of the headteacher ....

The books of the children ....

The cars of the teachers ....

2 marks

10 Add the suffixes '**er**' or '**est**' to the adjectives in the brackets to complete the sentences.

You are .... (short) than your brother.

This is the .... (early) I have ever been up.

2 marks

11 Add a **suffix** to these words so that the sentences make sense.

There was great **excite** .... on the day of the school party.

He was extremely **thank** .... that the term was nearly over.

2 marks

12 Tick the **two** sentences where the **apostrophe** has been used correctly.

You're cat is in my house. ☐

My dog's paw is sore. ☐

It's time for your supper. ☐

I love your new roller skate's. ☐

2 marks

3

Page Total

Year 4 Grammar & Punctuation

Summer Assessment

13 Circle the correct form of the **present perfect tense** in the sentences below.

I **have eaten** / **have ate** all the cabbage on my plate.

Ibrahim **is finished** / **has finished** the test.

2 marks

14 Rewrite the sentence below with the correct **punctuation**.

I cant go to my friends house

....

1 mark

End of Summer Assessment

Page Total

TOTAL

/ 25

PERCENTAGE SCORE

%

Year 4 Grammar & Punctuation

Optional Test 1

Name .... Class .... Date ....

1 Rewrite these sentences putting in any missing **punctuation** including **capital letters**.

mrs khan takes the class on a friday

....

have you read any roald dahl books

....

3 marks

2 Complete the sentences with the most appropriate **conjunctions** from the box.

but	so	or	and

Would you like coffee .... would you prefer tea?

She tried to get tickets for the match ....they were sold out.

Jude wasn't feeling well .... he stayed in bed.

2 marks

3 Add a **full stop**, **question mark** or **exclamation mark** at the end of these sentences.

What a lovely surprise ☐

This book is very interesting ☐

Have you got any pets ☐

2 marks

1

Page Total

Year 4 Grammar & Punctuation

Optional Test 1

4 Use the **prepositions** in the box to complete the sentences below.

inside	through	across

The dog was sleeping .... its kennel.

He had to climb .... the window to get in the house.

We walked .... the wooden bridge.

2 marks

5 Choose words to show that the order of the sentences below is correct. You can use a combination of **conjunctions**, **prepositions** and **adverbs** to express time. (The first one has been done for you.)

First .... she put the toothpaste on her toothbrush.

.... she turned on the tap and began brushing her teeth.

.... her teeth were thoroughly clean, she rinsed out her mouth.

.... she turned off the tap and smiled into the mirror.

2 marks

6 Add an appropriate **pronoun** in the space provided. (The first one has been done for you.)

These felt-tips belong to <u>us</u>. They are .... ours ....

<u>The children</u> walked in single file. .... were very well behaved.

That is <u>Eva's</u> magazine. It is ....

The teacher told off <u>Henry and Habeeb</u>. He was very cross with ....

2 marks

Page Total

Year 4 Grammar & Punctuation

Optional Test 1

7 Rewrite the **verbs** in the sentences below in the **past tense**. (Just write the verbs.)

The visitor speaks to the children in assembly.

....

He reads every night for a week.

....

I think about giving my pocket money to charity.

....

3 marks

---

8 Circle the correct form of the **progressive tense** in the sentences below.

I **walk** / **am walking** to school with my best friend.

She **was collecting** / **collected** all the exercise books at the end of the lesson.

2 marks

---

9 Correct the following sentences so that they are written in **Standard English**.

I have brung my swimming kit today.

....

I done my detention yesterday.

....

2 marks

3

Page Total

Year 4 Grammar & Punctuation

Optional Test 1

---

10 Circle the correct form of the **present perfect tense**.

Lily and Leo **has / have** got the same pump bag.

1 mark

---

11 Put **speech marks** (**inverted commas**) into the sentence below.

What have you done to your jumper? Mum asked.

1 mark

---

12 Put a circle round the **three adverbs** in the words below.

quickly   pretty   under   fish

happily   orange   sometimes

2 marks

---

13 Find similar words to replace the **verbs** in the following sentences.
(The first one has been done for you.)

Leona **walked** to the shops ....**marched**............

Zain **ran** down the corridor ....

Alex **looked** inside the drawer ....

2 marks

---

14 Change the **structure** of this sentence so that it starts with the underlined **conjunction**.

It was still raining although the sun was shining.

....

2 marks

4

Page Total

Year 4 Grammar & Punctuation

Optional Test 1

---

15 Choose **two** appropriate **adjectives** from the list below to describe the nouns in the sentences.

metal	furry	small	old

The .... kitten was so cute.

The .... gate was starting to rust.

1 mark

---

16 Complete the sentence below with an appropriate **subordinate clause**.

This is the girl who ....

1 mark

---

17 Extend the sentence below with a **noun phrase** to describe the alien.

The spaceman saw a green alien with ....

1 mark

---

18 Underline the **determiner** in the sentence below.

Josh watched an eagle swoop down.

1 mark

5

Page Total

Year 4 Grammar & Punctuation

Optional Test 1

19 Join the beginning and the end of each sentence with the correct **conjunction**. (The first one has been done for you.)

We learnt to swim   unless   it is raining.

I did my homework   because   you give me back my pencil.

I'm not talking to you   before   you were playing outside.

It will be indoor play   while   we started school.

2 marks

20 Rewrite the sentence placing the **adverbial phrase** at the beginning.

She delivered the message as quickly as possible.

....

1 mark

21 Identify the different **word classes** (parts of speech) by putting the following words under the correct headings.

inside	pencil	because	quietly	their	hid	strong

noun	verb	adjective	adverb
....	....	....	....

preposition	pronoun	conjunction
....	....	....

2 marks

22 Are the underlined clauses **coordinating clauses** or **subordinate clauses**? Circle the correct option.

The postman bit the dog <u>which had been barking</u>.

coordinating / subordinate

I've had my hair cut, <u>but I don't like the new style</u>.

coordinating / subordinate

2 marks

6

Page Total

23 Add your own **prefix** or **suffix** so that the words make sense within the sentence.

Shana thought it was very ....**fair** that she had never been chosen for the school netball team.

Our new sofa is so **comfort**................ everyone wants to sit on it.

2 marks

24 Rewrite the underlined words using the **apostrophe for contraction**.

I <u>have not</u> been to school today because <u>I have</u> not been feeling well. I <u>will not</u> be going to school tomorrow either.

....

2 marks

25 Write the **plural** form of each of the following **nouns**.

brush ....   toy ....

baby ....   tooth ....

2 marks

26 Underline the **subordinate clause** in the sentence below.

The car raced off when the lights turned green.

1 mark

Page Total

Year 4 Grammar & Punctuation

Optional Test 1

27 Write each phrase using the correct **apostrophe for possession**.
(The first one has been done for you.)

the dresses of the girls   the girls' dresses

the handbag of the lady   ....

the prizes of the children   ....

the car of the teacher   ....

2 marks

28 Add **prefixes** or **suffixes** to make **three** new words that belong to the same **word family**.

friend   ....

                ....

2 marks

End of Optional Test 1

Page Total

TOTAL

/ 50

PERCENTAGE SCORE

%

Year 4 Grammar & Punctuation

Optional Test 2

Name .... Class .... Date ....

1 Rewrite these sentences putting in any missing **punctuation** including **capital letters**.

have you been to spain or france for your holidays

....

we went to australia for all of august

....

3 marks

2 Complete the sentences with the most appropriate **conjunctions** from the box.

but	so	or	and

Should I sell my old video games .... should I keep them?

We didn't want to miss the bus ....we left the house in plenty of time.

Ava wanted to join the group .... the boys wouldn't let her.

2 marks

3 Add a **full stop**, **question mark** or **exclamation mark** at the end of these sentences.

Get off my foot ☐

When do you finish work ☐

I would like to hear more of your story ☐

2 marks

1

Page Total

Year 4 Grammar & Punctuation

Optional Test 2

4 Use the **prepositions** in the box to complete the sentences below.

over	along	after

The cat was creeping .... the fence.

He had to climb .... the wall to get into the garden.

We left school .... our drama lesson.

2 marks

5 Choose words to show that the order of the sentences below is correct. You can use a combination of **conjunctions**, **prepositions** and **adverbs** to express time. (The first one has been done for you.)

<u>First</u>........... put the dirty dishes in the dishwasher.

.... put in a dishwasher tablet and switch on the dishwasher.

.... the dishwasher bleeps, the dishes will be clean.

.... open the dishwasher door and put the clean dishes away.

2 marks

6 Add an appropriate **pronoun** in the space provided. (The first one has been done for you.)

This pencil case is <u>Jake's</u>. It is ....<u>his</u>................ .

Do you want <u>your</u> bag back? It is ....

<u>Maria</u> doesn't want to talk to you. .... doesn't want to be your friend.

<u>I</u> have had that pencil sharpener all year. It is ....

2 marks

2

Year 4 Grammar & Punctuation

7 Rewrite the **verbs** in the sentences below in the **past tense**. (Just write the verbs.)

She catches the ball very well.

....

She throws the sweet wrapper in the bin.

....

The bird flies down from the tree.

....

3 marks

8 Circle the correct form of the **progressive tense** in the sentences below.

The boys **help** / **are helping** to clean up.

They **were skipping** / **skipped** on the playground.

2 marks

9 Correct the following sentences so that they are written in **Standard English**.

She should of gone to the party.

....

I'm not going nowhere.

....

2 marks

Page Total

Year 4 Grammar & Punctuation

Optional Test 2

10 Circle the correct form of the **present perfect tense**.

Alex **has / have** got a lot of superhero figures.

1 mark

11 Put **speech marks** (**inverted commas**) into the sentence below.

Where should I hang my coat? Finley asked.

1 mark

12 Put a circle round the **three adverbs** in the words below.

bad   silently   between   suddenly

fancy   always   wicked

2 marks

13 Find similar words to replace the **verbs** in the following sentences. (The first one has been done for you.)

The squirrel <u>ran</u> across the lawn.   darted ....

Jermaine <u>closed</u> the door.   ....

The cat <u>jumped</u> over the wall   ....

2 marks

14 Change the **structure** of this sentence so that it starts with the underlined **conjunction**.

I won't give you a biscuit <u>unless</u> you ask nicely.

....

2 marks

4

Page Total

Year 4 Grammar & Punctuation

Optional Test 2

15 Choose **two** appropriate **adjectives** from the list below to describe the nouns in the sentences.

gold	round	small	shiny

The .... ring was just what she wanted.

He threw the .... ball.

1 mark

16 Complete the sentence below with an appropriate **subordinate clause**.

That's the dog which ....

1 mark

17 Extend the sentence below with a **noun phrase** to describe the girl.

I spoke to the little girl with ....

1 mark

18 Underline the **determiner** in the sentence below.

Do those shoes belong to you?

1 mark

Page Total

Year 4 Grammar & Punctuation

Optional Test 2

19 Join the beginning and the end of each sentence with the correct **conjunction**. (The first one has been done for you.)

You're not allowed on the PlayStation   while   you start behaving yourself.

We always do a maths test   until   you helped me.

I'll vacuum the carpet   because   you mop the kitchen floor.

I'll help you with your homework   before   we go out for morning play.

2 marks

20 Rewrite the sentence placing the **adverbial phrase** at the beginning.

He got out of bed at the crack of dawn.

....

1 mark

21 Identify the different **word classes** (parts of speech) by putting the following words under the correct headings.

loudly	under	knocked	they	yellow	although	door

noun   **verb**   **adjective**   **adverb**

....

preposition   **pronoun**   **conjunction**

....

2 marks

22 Are the underlined clauses **coordinating clauses** or **subordinate clauses**? Circle the correct option.

I went on holiday with a suitcase <u>which weighed 24 kg</u>.

coordinating / subordinate

My teacher gave me a sticker, <u>but I didn't really deserve it</u>.

coordinating / subordinate

2 marks

6

Page Total

Year 4 Grammar & Punctuation

23 Add your own **prefix** or **suffix** so that the words make sense within the sentence.

Bartek thought the mathematics problem was .... **possible** to solve.

Please be **care** .... as you carry that hot cup of tea.

2 marks

24 Rewrite the underlined words using the **apostrophe for contraction**.

<u>You are </u>not hungry, are you? <u>You will</u> have to wait because Mum <u>is not</u> home yet.

....

2 marks

25 Write the **plural** form of each of the following **nouns**.

box   ....   person   ....

leaf   ....   table   ....

2 marks

26 Underline the **subordinate clause** in the sentence below.

He went outside to play after he had finished his tea.

1 mark

Page Total

Year 4 Grammar & Punctuation

Optional Test 2

27 Write each phrase using the correct **apostrophe for possession**.
(The first one has been done for you.)

the gloves of the girl → **the girl's gloves**

the pictures of the artists → ....

the shoes of the men → ....

the tail of the dog → ....

2 marks

28 Add **prefixes** or **suffixes** to make **three** new words that belong to the same **word family**.

excite ....

....

2 marks

End of Optional Test 2

Page Total

TOTAL
/ 50

PERCENTAGE SCORE
%

8

Year 4 Grammar & Punctuation

Optional Test 3

Name .... Class .... Date ....

1 Rewrite these sentences putting in any missing **punctuation** including **capital letters**.

The train for london departs every tuesday

....

will it be stopping at wigan and crewe

....

3 marks

2 Complete the sentences with the most appropriate **conjunctions** from the box.

but	so	or	and

Anna wanted to go to the party .... her dad said she couldn't go.

I might play out with Harry .... I might just stay at home.

I really wanted the pizza .... I pushed to the front of the queue.

2 marks

3 Add a **full stop**, **question mark** or **exclamation mark** at the end of these sentences.

I'll have a biscuit, please ☐

Why are you doing that ☐

That hurts ☐

2 marks

1

Year 4 Grammar & Punctuation

Optional Test 3

4 Use the **prepositions** in the box to complete the sentences below.

before	behind	during

Javed was hiding .... the curtain.

Rhiannon talked non-stop .... the maths lesson.

We washed our hands .... we went in to dinner.

2 marks

5 Choose words to show that the order of the sentences below is correct. You can use a combination of **conjunctions**, **prepositions** and **adverbs** to express time. (The first one has been done for you.)

<u>First</u>.......... put the plug in the plughole and fill the bath with hot water.

.... mix with cold water until it is the right temperature.

.... the water is the right depth, turn off the taps.

.... enjoy a relaxing bath.

2 marks

6 Add an appropriate **pronoun** in the space provided. (The first one has been done for you.)

That ball belongs to <u>Frankie and Bernie</u>. It is ....<u>theirs</u>............. .

I've got your <u>diary</u>. Do you want .... back?

That belongs to <u>Fern and me</u>. It is ....

Hello, <u>Toby</u>. How are ....?

2 marks

2

Page Total

Year 4 Grammar & Punctuation

7 Rewrite the **verbs** in the sentences below in the **past tense**. (Just write the verbs.)

The robber steals a ring from the jewellery shop.

....

I go to the park with my older brother.

....

The teacher teaches us some French words.

....

3 marks

8 Circle the correct form of the **progressive tense** in the sentences below.

The dog **chases** / **is chasing** the cat.

The children **were following** / **followed** the teacher.

2 marks

9 Correct the following sentences so that they are written in **Standard English**.

They does everything wrong.

....

It were a silly thing to do!

....

2 marks

Page Total

Year 4 Grammar & Punctuation

Optional Test 3

10 Circle the correct form of the **present perfect tense**.

Ricky and Daniel **has / have** worked hard all day.

1 mark

11 Put **speech marks** (**inverted commas**) into the sentence below.

Will you go with me to the school office? Polina asked.

1 mark

12 Put a circle round the **three adverbs** in the words below.

bravely   honest   cheese

because   above   politely   often

2 marks

13 Find similar words to replace the **verbs** in the following sentences.
(The first one has been done for you.)

Charlotte <u>laughed</u> at the teacher's joke.   chuckled ....

Arun <u>ran</u> very fast.   ....

Adam <u>bellowed</u> at the top of his voice.   ....

2 marks

14 Change the **structure** of this sentence so that it starts with the underlined **conjunction**.

You can't have your phone back <u>until</u> you say sorry.

....

2 marks

4

Page Total

© Copyright HeadStart Primary Ltd

Year 4 Grammar & Punctuation

15 Choose **two** appropriate **adjectives** from the list below to describe the nouns in the sentences.

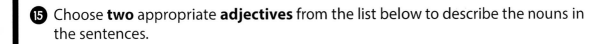

| young | wooden | handsome | green |

The .... door slowly creaked open.

The .... man showed me to my seat.

1 mark

16 Complete the sentence below with an appropriate **subordinate clause**.

This is the book that ....

1 mark

17 Extend the sentence below with a **noun phrase** to describe the dog.

I stroked the big dog with ....

1 mark

18 Underline the **determiner** in the sentence below.

I go there every day.

1 mark

Page Total

Year 4 Grammar & Punctuation

Optional Test 3

19 Join the beginning and the end of each sentence with the correct **conjunction**. (The first one has been done for you.)

We went in the swimming pool | because | I have a go on the scooter.

You can have one of my sweets | after | you have been kind to me.

We're both in trouble | while | we had a shower.

You can wear my rollerblades | unless | you tell the truth.

2 marks

20 Rewrite the sentence placing the **adverbial phrase** at the beginning.

I heard the bad news later that day.

....

1 mark

21 Identify the different **word classes** (parts of speech) by putting the following words under the correct headings.

| favourite | above | quickly | ruler | whistled | because | her |

noun   **verb**   **adjective**   **adverb**

....

preposition   **pronoun**   **conjunction**

....

2 marks

22 Are the underlined clauses **coordinating clauses** or **subordinate clauses**? Circle the correct option.

I ran all the way, <u>but I was still late for school</u>. **coordinating / subordinate**

I believed the story <u>which she told me at lunchtime</u>.

coordinating / subordinate

2 marks

6

Page Total

Year 4 Grammar & Punctuation

Optional Test 3

23 Add your own **prefix** or **suffix** so that the words make sense within the sentence.

Layla told me it was ....**honest** to take the money from the drawer.

Neha said that the puncture made her bicycle **use** ....

2 marks

24 Rewrite the underlined words using the **apostrophe for contraction**.

<u>Do not</u> go on the grass! <u>There is</u> a sign to say that you <u>must not</u> go on it.

....

2 marks

25 Write the **plural** form of each of the following **nouns**.

tree   ....   branch ....

life   ....   sheep   ....

2 marks

26 Underline the **subordinate clause** in the sentence below.

Year 3 went out to play before the bell went.

1 mark

Page Total

Year 4 Grammar & Punctuation

27 Write each phrase using the correct **apostrophe for possession**. (The first one has been done for you.)

the whiskers of the cat
the cat's whiskers

the costumes of the actors
....

the hats of the women
....

the roar of the giant
....

2 marks

28 Add **prefixes** or **suffixes** to make **three** new words that belong to the same **word family**.

agree
....

....

2 marks

End of Optional Test 3

Page Total

TOTAL

/ 50

PERCENTAGE SCORE

%

8

Answers

Activity Sheets
& Assessments/Tests

Raw score/scaled score
conversion charts for the
Optional Tests are supplied
on the CD-ROM.

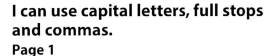

Answers – Activity Sheets

I can use capital letters, full stops and commas.
Page 1

The young King Arthur served as Sir Kay's squire in the story of the 'Sword in the Stone'.

Squires had to develop strength, speed, agility and leadership skills.

It was also his duty to learn about courtly etiquette, jousting, music and dancing.

The squire not only had to serve the knight in times of peace, but he also had to follow him on to the battlefield in times of war.

Sir Lancelot, Sir Percival, Sir Galahad and Sir Kay were all Knights of the Round Table.

I can use conjunctions to extend sentences.
Page 2

A noble's son could train to be a knight > when > he was seven years old.

He would first need to train as a page > before > being appointed a squire.

A squire would train with weapons > but > he also needed to know how to serve at table.

A knight would protect the weak > and > be courteous to noblewomen.

Noblemen's sons became pages **because** one day they wanted to be a knight.

The squire had to teach the pages **although** he also had to wait on the knight.

The squire trained in swordsmanship **so** he could fight with the knight in battle.

The squire also had to learn about music **and** he needed to study the arts.

Any boy could become a squire, **but** it helped if you came from noble birth.

I can use full stops, question marks and exclamation marks.
Page 3

Where did you put my helmet?
Saddle my horse now!
Would you like me to accompany you to the feast?
I've been hurt!
Have you cleaned my armour?
I am at your service, my lady.
Forward into battle!
This is my young squire.
What have you done with my sword?

I can use prepositions.
Page 4

<u>over</u>	<u>in</u>	but	however
<u>inside</u>	<u>below</u>	buried	when
<u>under</u>	<u>to</u>	if	<u>around</u>
because	**before**	**through**	**behind**

The army lays siege **to** the castle.
The knights camp **outside** the castle walls.
Huge mangonels hurl stones and rocks **over** the battlements.
The knights climb **up** wooden towers called belfries.
Meanwhile, miners tunnel **under** the castle walls.
The knights **inside** the castle fire arrows **through** the arrow slits.
Sometimes they pour burning oil on the army **below**.

I can use words to express time.
Page 5

First, find your seat at one of the long tables.
Then remain standing until the king has entered.
When the king has sat down, you may also sit.
Before you eat, wash your hands in the bowl of water when it is passed to you.
After you have washed your hands, you may begin to eat.
Now tuck in as quickly as you can. (The food doesn't hang around for long!)

1

While you are eating, help yourself to plenty of wine.
Next, wipe your fingers on your sleeve. (Napkins are not provided at a medieval banquet!)
Later, throw the bones on the floor for the dogs.
Finally, fall asleep on one of the tables with your face in a trencher!

I can use pronouns.
Page 6

At school **we** did an assembly about King Arthur and the Knights of the Round Table. Miss told **us** that **he** had a round table so that the knights wouldn't fight over who sat next to **him**. **They** were a jealous lot back then! **I** took my wooden sword into school because **I** was going to play the part of Sir Lancelot. **He** was one of the most famous of the knights. My friend George was going to play the part of King Arthur. Unfortunately, George and **I** fell out. My sword was bigger than **his** but George said **he** should have the biggest one because **he** was the king. When **I** wasn't looking George picked up my sword and began to wave **it** about.
"Hey! That's **mine**!" I shouted. "Not **yours**! Give it back to **me**!" and **I** hit **him** over the head.
"Get off **me**!" he shouted back. "**I** hate **you**!"
The children watching laughed. **They** thought it was part of the play. Miss didn't find it so amusing though and **she** kept **us** in during playtime. **We** weren't given big parts to play in class assemblies ever again.

I can identify the present and past tense of verbs.
Page 7

The majority of people in the medieval period <u>lived</u> in the country and <u>laboured</u> in the fields as farmers. They <u>grew</u> crops such as barley, wheat and oats. They sometimes <u>kept</u> animals such as chickens, pigs and cows. They <u>gave</u> most of what they <u>earned</u> to the local lord who <u>owned</u> the land. They mostly <u>ate</u> vegetables. They <u>had</u> very hard lives.
It <u>wasn't</u> much easier in the city. Most towns and cities <u>suffered</u> from overcrowding and they <u>were</u> very dirty. Here they <u>worked</u> as craftsmen and <u>belonged</u> to a guild. Young boys <u>served</u> as apprentices for seven years learning their craft. Other jobs <u>included</u> servants, merchants and bakers.
Some lords and their families <u>resided</u> in spacious castles, but most people <u>dwelt</u> in small one or two-room homes. The whole family often <u>slept</u> together in the one room and sometimes <u>shared</u> the room with their animals. It <u>could</u> be very smelly! In winter they <u>snuggled</u> up to the pigs just to stay warm!

I can use the present progressive and past progressive tense.
Page 8

The young page **was filling** the cup with wine when he sneezed.
The squire **was cleaning** the weapons when he saw the blood on the sword.
The squire **was waiting** to help the knight when he dismounted the horse.
The knights **were riding** up to the castle when the guards lowered the drawbridge.
While the ladies **were dancing** to the music, the fool did cartwheels.
While the guests **were eating** and drinking, the traitor sneaked into the hall.
When nobody **was looking**, the assassin put poison in the king's cup.
The king **was fighting** for his life as the assailant silently crept away.

I can make the auxiliary verb and the main verb agree.
Page 9

He is sat in the stand watching the jousting.
He is sitting in the stand watching the jousting. ✓
We were serving the lord in the Great Hall. ✓
We was serving the lord in the Great Hall.

At this very moment, the young page **is** serving breakfast to the knight.
Before that he **was** helping the knight to get dressed.
Everyone can see that the knight **is** wearing his armour back-to-front.
The squire **was** laughing when he realised his mistake.

2

Earlier on today, we **were** preparing for the jousting tournament.

The young knight **was** practising his skills on the tilting field yesterday.

The day before, the king **was** watching the knights practising from his pavilion.

Now you **are** watching the tournament from the stands.

I can use Standard English when writing verbs. (1)
Page 10

The lady of the manor **was brushing** her hair as breakfast was served.

Her maids **were helping** her to get dressed for prayers in the chapel.

She **was saying** her prayers in the chapel when the knight arrived.

Throughout the morning she **was sitting** in her chamber doing her needlework.

Later, she **was standing** by her husband's side as he collected the rent.

At supper, she ate pheasant as the musicians **were playing**.

In the evening, she **was dancing** with the young courtiers.

I can use Standard English when writing verbs. (2)
Page 11

The doctor's assistant **has** collected pond leeches.

The chimney sweep **have** climbed castle chimneys.

The fullers **have** washed the wool with urine.

The squire **has** cleaned the blood off the armour.

The groom of the stool **has** carried the commode.

The gong farmers **have** emptied the latrine pit.

The cupbearer **has** tasted the drink for poison.

The barber also **has** pulled out rotting teeth.

I can use Standard English when writing verbs. (3)
Page 12

I **have ridden** my horse across the stream.

He **has eaten** pigeon pie for supper.

I **have seen** the knight kiss the lady.

He **has broken** the sword in two.

I **have known** the knight for years.

The page **has grown** into a handsome knight.

I **have gone** across the drawbridge.

I **have drunk** a jug of mead.

The maid **has sung** a sweet song.

I can use speech marks in direct speech.
Page 13

The squire said, "It's time to get up for work, my lord."

The knight said, "Go away! It's the middle of the night!"

The squire said, "I know, my lord."

The knight asked, "Then what is the reason for waking me up at this unearthly hour?"

The squire replied, "You're on the knight shift!"

I can change direct speech to reported speech.
Page 14

The knight said that he had come to kill the dragon.

The dragon said that he didn't want any more tinned food.

Sir Cumference said that he was the fattest knight in the kingdom.

Sir Prize said that he had a practical joke for the king.

The mother asked her son why he wanted to go to Camelot.

He replied that he wanted to go for the knight life.

I can identify and use adverbs.
Page 15

It was a wet and wild evening when the knight bravely rode up to the sinister-looking inn on the outskirts of the town. The wooden sign, "George and the Dragon", creaked noisily as it flapped back and forth in the gathering storm. He boldly went up to the door and knocked loudly. He waited patiently for the sound of approaching footsteps, but none came.

He courageously rapped on the door again. This time a window above suddenly crashed open and a woman's head unexpectedly emerged, her face contorted with anger.

"What's the meaning of waking me up at this time of night?" she shrieked crossly.

3

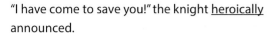

"I have come to save you!" the knight <u>heroically</u> announced.

"Clear off!" she <u>rudely</u> shouted back down at him. "I don't need saving!"

"I have heard that there is someone in distress that needs rescuing," he uttered <u>unsurely</u>.

"There's no one in this inn needs rescuing!" she <u>angrily</u> replied. "Now beat it!" She shook her fist at him <u>threateningly</u>. "Or I'll fetch my chamber pot!" she added <u>ominously</u>.

"Is there anyone else in the inn?" he asked <u>uncertainly</u>.

"Just me and my husband," she replied as she <u>quickly</u> retreated back into the room.

The knight <u>promptly</u> looked back at the name on the sign that was now swinging <u>violently</u> to and fro in the wind.

"Can I speak to your husband George then?" he managed to ask <u>politely</u> before the contents of the chamber pot were <u>crudely</u> emptied all over him.

I can identify and use alternative verbs.
Page 16

Sir Vival, a knight of St George, was **returning** from the Crusades on a cold, dark winter's night when his old, faithful horse, which had **journeyed** many miles, **collapsed** and **expired**. Sir Vival **collected** what belongings he could and **trudged** towards a light in the distance. He **marched** up to the door of the inn and **rapped** loudly.

"A horse! A horse! I must have a horse!" he **bellowed**. The door was **unbolted** and a young girl **appeared**.

"I **beg** your pardon, good knight," she **answered**, "but my father and my brothers have **departed** to go hunting in the forest and have **taken** all the horses. They haven't **informed** me when they will **return**."

"Are there no other horses for me to **mount**?" he **enquired** desperately.

"I don't **believe** there are other horses hereabout," the girl **responded**, "but sometimes my brothers ride our Great Dane dog when the need arises. Would that be of any help?"

"**Conduct** me to the animal," the knight **spoke** wearily. In the sleet and rain the girl **escorted** the knight to the back of the inn to the stables where she **vanished** inside. She **emerged guiding** a massive dog which was quite big enough to ride. However, he was old, his coat was threadbare and he **staggered** on his spindly legs. The knight **stared** at the young girl disbelievingly and said, "You wouldn't **dispatch** a knight on a dog like this!"

I can construct sentences in different ways.
Page 17

If you were rich in the medieval period, there were lots of festivals to enjoy.

Because there were so many feast days, banquets were held often.

While the guests ate their food, musicians would play.

As the various courses were being served, a jester would amuse the guests.

After they had feasted, acrobats, fire-eaters and conjurors entertained the guests.

When the tables were cleared, there would be dancing.

If the ladies requested it, the knights were expected to dance.

If you were one of the servants, it was a lot of hard work!

I can identify and use paired adjectives. (1 & 2)
Pages 18 & 19

Children draw and describe their own mythical monster.

I can identify a clause within a sentence.
Page 20

Once upon a time in a castle, **which was far, far away**, there was a beautiful princess.

The beautiful princess, **who was actually rather vain and conceited**, had many admirers. One day she gazed out of her window, **which was at the top of the tallest tower**, to see a queue of knights. The knights, **who were in their finest suits of armour**, were all wanted to marry her. They were patiently waiting to see the king, **who was a bit of a joker**, to ask for his daughter's hand in marriage. The king, **who could never make his mind up**, decided to send the knights out on a quest.

Whichever knight could bring back an egg of a dragon, **that he had vanquished in a battle**, could have the hand of his daughter. (I really don't know why they wouldn't want the rest of her!)

A young knight, **who was called Sir Tainwyn**, (think about it!), had a plan to get the dragon egg without losing his life. He rode up to the mountain, **where the dragon had his lair**, and requested a meeting. To demonstrate his honour he had left his sword, **which usually went everywhere with him**, back at the castle. He told the dragon, **who was a surprisingly friendly fellow**, he would swap a dragon egg for whatever the dragon desired.

I can use the relative pronouns 'who', 'that' and 'which'.
Page 21

Puff the dragon, <u>who</u> was a gentle creature, lived by the sea.
One of the dragons, <u>which</u> had been sleeping in the dormant volcano, rose up into the sky.
The sword, <u>which</u> had smashed against the dragon's scales, broke into a thousand pieces.
The sword, <u>that</u> was found buried in the sand, had magical powers.
The squire, <u>who</u> had slain the dragon, became a famous knight.
The shield, <u>that</u> had saved the knight's life, had been burnt to cinders.
The horse, <u>which</u> was a favourite of the knight, had gone lame.
Warrior, <u>who</u> was a war horse, carried knights into battle.

I can recognise countable and non-countable nouns.
Page 22

<u>Countable</u>	<u>Non-countable</u>
sword	bravery
mountain	fear
castle	honesty
muscles	sky
wound	strength
knight	evil
shield	happiness
egg	beauty
dragon	kindness

I can identify and use noun phrases.
Page 23

The warlock lived in <u>the dark castle on the hill</u>.
<u>A grotesque creature with fang-like teeth</u> attacked the knight.
The princess was locked in <u>the tower hidden by a dense forest</u>.
<u>The lady in the blue headdress</u> danced with all the courtiers.
The knight was <u>a man of honour</u>.
<u>The young page with the shaking hands</u> dropped the broth.

(The following are suggestions only.)

The blacksmith with **the huge muscles** bent the iron bar in half.
The princess in **the tall tower** waited to be rescued.
The king **with the terrible temper** ordered that all the prisoners should be beheaded.
The queen dressed in **the satin gown** gave her favour to the knight.
Because the knight was a man of **his word** he could never tell a lie.
The dragon with **the green scales** raised its head and roared.

I can use a range of linking words or phrases.
Page 24

The brothers Triston and Raymond were both squires, **although** their lives couldn't have been more different. **On the one hand**, they were close in age and looked very similar. **On the other hand**, they had very different personalities. Triston was hard working, obedient and responsible, **but** Raymond was lazy, argumentative and was always up to mischief. **Yet**, despite all his shortcomings, Raymond had an excellent sense of humour, which would prove useful in the end. **Even though** sword fighting was dangerous and tiring, Triston would practise his skills all day long **until** he got them right. **In contrast**, Raymond would soon give up and would run off to the stables to practise his juggling. **While** Triston was up early in the morning preparing the knight's breakfast, Raymond would be fast asleep in bed. **Because** Triston was so determined and conscientious he was quickly made into a knight. **However**, Raymond was just not cut out for the responsibility. **Consequently**, Triston became a brave and dashing knight, **whereas** Raymond decided his talents lay elsewhere and he became the court jester.

I can use a range of prepositions.
Page 25

The court jester or fool could be found <u>at</u> court entertaining the king and queen.

He would wear brightly coloured clothes and a hat <u>with</u> bells <u>upon</u> it.

Queen Elizabeth I had a fool that often sat <u>by</u> her side.

Some would sing and play musical instruments. Others could juggle and walk <u>on</u> stilts.

As well as making jokes, they would often say things that came <u>into</u> their heads.

Henry VIII's fool would often give bad news <u>to</u> him, which no one else would dare.

The balls have landed: <u>between</u> his feet, <u>under</u> a table, <u>beside</u> a chest, <u>in front</u> of a chest, <u>behind</u> a chest, <u>inside</u> a bowl of fruit, <u>on top</u> of his head, <u>through</u> a window.

I can change statements into questions.
Page 26

Did the jester juggle his balls?

Can he also play the lute?

Was Henry the VIII's jester called Will Sommer?

Did Shakespeare write about fools in his plays?

Were Jesters popular in Ancient Egypt as well as Medieval England?

Can the joker or jester be seen in a pack of playing cards?

I can use fronted adverbials.
Page 27

Sweetly, the troubadour sang to the beautiful music.

Elegantly, the lady danced the quadrille all through the evening.

Energetically, the jester danced the jig to entertain the guests.

Enthusiastically, the musicians played during the banquet.

Carelessly, the serving girl spilt the wine over the king.

Furiously, the king shouted at her and demanded that she leave.

Timidly, she cleaned up the mess and left crying.

I can use fronted adverbial phrases.
Page 28

Quickly and quietly, he slipped across the drawbridge.

Silent and forbidding, the dark tower loomed in front of them.

Before sunset, the knight reached the castle.

As fast as he could, he polished the armour.

Outside the city walls, he found a bloodstained banner.

In the depth of winter, you need to wear a fur cloak.

In the middle of the night, the castle was attacked.

I can identify and use adverbs that do not end in 'ly'.
Page 29

People were punished <u>hard</u> for committing crimes in medieval times.

The accused didn't spend <u>long</u> in gaol.

They went <u>straight</u> to court and trial by jury.

For minor crimes, people were <u>often</u> placed in the stocks.

For more serious crimes, people would <u>always</u> end up losing a body part.

For very serious crimes, they would <u>almost</u> certainly end up losing their head.

The executioner had to strike the neck <u>well</u>.

Executioners <u>often</u> took several blows before the head was removed from the body.

Anne Boleyn decided she would <u>rather</u> die by the sword than the axe.

I imagine she slept <u>little</u> the night before her execution!

(More and very are also adverbs that may be identified)

I can identify different word classes
Page 30

Castles were first built by the <u>Normans</u> in the 11th century. – **proper noun**

There are still lots of <u>castles</u> all over Britain that you can visit. – **common noun**

The Normans <u>built</u> castles to help them defend the land that they had conquered. – **verb**

6

They were <u>often</u> built on hills so the enemy could be seen from far away. – **adverb**

Castles were often <u>damp</u> and draughty. – **adjective**

The main building was called the keep, <u>which</u> was protected by walls and towers. – **conjunction**

Often there was a deep ditch dug <u>around</u> the castle called the moat. – **preposition**

Prisoners <u>were</u> kept in the basements called the dungeons. – **auxiliary verb**

Toilets, called garderobes, were built along <u>the</u> inside of the castle walls. – **definite article**

<u>Everything</u> from the toilet dropped down into the castle moat. – **pronoun**

Lots of people were needed to keep the castle running <u>smoothly</u>. – **adverb**

It wasn't easy to attack a castle, <u>but</u> people tried anyway. – **conjunction**

<u>They</u> used siege towers, battering rams and trebuchets to attack the castle. – **pronoun**

<u>Victory</u> for the attacking side was rare. – **abstract noun**

I can identify and use alternative words.
Page 31

(Answers may vary.)

Dragons are among the world's most popular mythical <u>creatures</u>. **beasts**

They have a long and <u>interesting</u> history. **fascinating**

No one is quite sure when stories of dragons first <u>appeared</u>. **arrived**

But in all stories from the Greeks to the early Christians they were described as <u>huge</u>, flying serpents. **large**

In some cultures they were useful and protective, but by medieval times they were nearly always described as harmful and <u>dangerous</u>. **menacing**

When people in the past unearthed large bones they <u>mistook</u>, what we now know to be dinosaur bones for the bones of dragons. **confused**

Most people can <u>imagine</u> a dragon clearly in their heads. **picture**

They are very popular in books and <u>films</u> from "How to Train Your Dragon" through to "The Hobbit". **movies**

They typically <u>protect</u> hoards of treasure such as mountains of gold. **guard**

They nearly all breathe fire and can <u>fly</u> into the sky with gigantic wings. **soar**

I can identify and use the present perfect and the past perfect tense.
Page 32

When the king cut into the pie, he discovered that the cook **had hidden** four and twenty blackbirds inside it.

The maid said a blackbird **had pecked** off her nose when she was hanging out the clothes.

The young page **has learnt** how to read.

By the end of the evening, the queen **had danced** with all the Knights of the Round Table.

"I **haven't introduced** you to Sir Galahad," said the lady-in-waiting.

"I **have never rescued** a fair maiden," admitted the knight.

When the queen opened the pantry door, she realised that the knave of hearts **had stolen** the tarts.

The knave was arrested but he swore he **hadn't taken** the tarts.

The squire **hasn't mastered** the art of sword fighting yet.

I can tell the difference between a coordinating and a subordinating conjunction.
Page 33

Although he searched everywhere, the gaoler could not find the keys to the gaol. **subordinating**

The king told the fool to stop his jests and everyone agreed. **coordinating**

His arm was badly broken when he fought the Black Knight. **subordinating**

The court physician dressed his wounds, yet it wasn't enough to save his life. **coordinating**

The prince climbed to the top of the tower so he could rescue the princess. **coordinating**

While the music played, the page sneaked in through a side door. **subordinating**

The king went hunting, but the queen decided to stay at home. **coordinating**

They lit the fires in the castle because it was very cold. **subordinating**

7

I can use a range of prefixes.
Page 34

The warlock used magic to dis**appear** into a cloud of smoke.
The knight found it im**possible** to get close to the fire-breathing dragon.
He was able to hide using his magic in**visible** cloak.
The princess was very un**happy** to be locked in the tower.
The shield was an irr**egular** shape after the dragon damaged it.

I can use the apostrophe for contractions.
Page 35

I <u>haven't</u> been so humiliated in all my life! <u>I've</u> been outside this castle all night in the rain. I shouted to the guard, but I <u>couldn't</u> make myself heard and he <u>didn't</u> let down the drawbridge. <u>It's</u> rained non-stop and now <u>I'm</u> chilled to the bone. I <u>don't</u> care that <u>I'm</u> supposed to be rescuing the princess from the dragon. <u>I'll</u> not be fighting any dragons today. In fact I <u>won't</u> be fighting any dragons ever again if you <u>don't</u> help me soon. <u>Where's</u> my squire? <u>He's</u> going to be for it when I get my hands on him! <u>I'd</u> told him quite clearly my suit of armour needed oiling, but he <u>wasn't</u> listening. He <u>couldn't</u> have cared less. Now the rain has rusted the armour and I <u>can't</u> move! Somebody fetch a tin opener!

I can use regular and irregular plurals.
Page 36

Regular	Irregular
dwarf – dwarfs (or dwarves)	goose – geese
tower – towers	man – men
loaf – loaves	mouse – mice
city – cities	ox – oxen
church – churches	tooth – teeth
branch – branches	foot – feet
wizard – wizards	child – children
thief – thieves	person – people
wife – wives	louse – lice

I can identify the different parts of a sentence.
Page 37

<u>Arthur</u> was the first born son of King Uther Pendragon. – **subject**
<u>He</u> was heir to the throne. – **subject**
Merlin was worried about the <u>safety</u> of the young prince. – **object**
He took the <u>baby</u> to a safe place where he was raised in secret. – **object**
When King Uther died, <u>nobody</u> could agree who would be the next king. – **subject**
<u>Merlin</u> used his magic to set a sword into the stone. – **subject**
He wrote on the <u>stone</u> in letters of gold. – **object**
"<u>Whoso</u> pulleth out this sword of this stone is the rightwise born king of all England." – **subject**
Nobles came from far and wide to try to pull the <u>sword</u> from the stone. – **object**
Not even the strongest men could do <u>it</u>. **object**
When Arthur was fifteen, <u>Merlin</u> took him to a tournament. – **subject**
<u>Sir Kay</u> had lost his sword. – **subject**
Arthur went to fetch <u>him</u> one. – **object**
Arthur saw the <u>sword</u> in the stone and pulled it out. – **object**
The crowd cheered for <u>Arthur</u> when he was crowned king. – **object**

I can use the apostrophe for possession.
Page 38

the blacksmith's hammer
the bailiff's keys
the grooms' brushes
the ladies' headdresses
the laundress's washing tub
the falconer's birds of prey
the pages' hats
the knights' swords
the scribe's quills
the guardsmen's spears

I can use the apostrophe correctly. (1)
Page 39

There are many magical **legends** about Merlin the magician.

It's thought he came from a town in **Wales** called Caer Myrddin, which means **Merlin's** town.

He worked for four different **kings** including King Uther.

But **he's** best known as King **Arthur's** adviser.

However, Merlin had many **adventures** before working for King Arthur.

There are many **stories** about King Arthur and Merlin.

Merlin was responsible for **Arthur's** education when he was a boy.

If it **wasn't** for **Merlin's** scheming the crown **wouldn't** have been put on **Arthur's** head.

There are several **versions** of **Merlin's** death.

The most **famous** one is where the Lady of the Lake **uses Merlin's** own magic to entomb him in a rock.

I can use the apostrophe correctly. (2)
Page 40

You're working for the blacksmith.

It's an important job at the castle.

Your furnace needs more heat.

You're using the bellows.

You're leading in a horse

Its shoe needs mending.

Its armour is damaged.

It's a hard job repairing a **horse's** armour.

I can use regular and irregular adjectives to compare. (Standard English) (1)
Page 41

(Either version is acceptable)

clever –

| cleverer | cleverest | *or* | more clever | most clever |

gentle –

| gentler | gentlest | *or* | more gentle | most gentle |

narrow –

| narrower | narrowest | *or* | more narrow | most narrow |

polite –

| politer | politest | *or* | more polite | most polite |

quiet –

| quieter | quietest | *or* | more quiet | most quiet |

simple –

| simpler | simplest | *or* | more simple | most simple |

friendly –

| friendlier | friendliest | *or* | more friendly | most friendly |

handsome –

| handsomer | handsomest |
| *or* | more handsome | most handsome |

I can use regular and irregular adjectives to compare. (Standard English) (2)
Page 42

The adjectives to compare should be formed as follows:

long	longer	longest
short	shorter	shortest
heavy	heavier	heaviest
light	lighter	lightest
fast	faster	fastest
slow	slower	slowest
big	bigger	biggest
small	smaller	smallest

Either version is acceptable for the following adjectives:

common	commoner	commonest	more common
common	most common
rare	rarer	rarest	more rare
most rare

I can use paragraphs to organise ideas. (1)
Page 43

Dear Lord Balderdash,

Please excuse my omissions and absent-mindedness in my previous correspondence. It was ridiculous of me to expect you to answer my ransom when I failed to give you my contact details. However, I have now put this matter right. So down to business!

I believe I made a small request for your title and lands in exchange for your daughter. I have now reconsidered this and I believe I was being far too generous. As well as your castle I think it's only fair you hand over all your worldly goods. (You can keep your wife!)

Please find enclosed a lock of your daughter's hair. Apart from this lock of hair she is still in one piece (for the time being!) However, I find her incredibly irritating and I'm not sure how long my patience will last. Send a knight with your answer and a pot of gold as a gesture of goodwill. You have forty-eight hours to reply.

By the way, the two fools you sent to rescue her are now locked up in the tower as well.

I can use paragraphs to organise ideas. (2)
Page 44

(Answers may vary.)

Once upon a time there was a beautiful princess. This beautiful princess, who was rather vain and conceited, had many admirers. One day she gazed out of her window to see a long queue of knights who were all eager to marry her. They were patiently waiting to see the king to ask him for his daughter's hand in marriage. The king, who liked playing pranks, decided to send the knights out on a quest. Whichever knight could bring back the egg of a dragon first could have the hand of his daughter. (I really don't know why they wouldn't want the rest of her!)

Many knights attempted the daring feat, but all returned fried (terri-fried!). A young knight, who was called Sir Tainwyn (think about it!), had a plan to get the dragon egg without turning into a burnt crisp. He rode up to the mountain, where the dragon had his lair, to request a meeting. First, he had to wake the dragon who (because of the nature of his work) had to sleep during the day. At first the dragon wasn't best pleased to be woken up but, when he saw that the knight was unarmed, he welcomed him into his cave for a chat.

The knight told him about his plan to swap a dragon egg for whatever the dragon desired. The dragon, who was a surprisingly friendly and amenable fellow, listened carefully and then informed him that, being a boy dragon, he didn't lay eggs and therefore couldn't help him with his request. However, he was a very practical dragon and he had a suggestion that would benefit them both.

Later that day, the knight rode back to the castle with a package under his arms, and announced that he had returned with dragon eggs. The whole court assembled in the throne room to watch him undo the package. He unwrapped an egg no bigger than a chicken's egg and, placing a string around it, pulled it across the floor to where the king was sitting. The king, perplexed, asked what he was doing for it was clearly not big enough to be a dragon egg. The knight replied, "Can you not see what I am doing? I'm dragon eggs behind me!" The king, who was a bit of a joker himself (I think I mentioned this), loved the practical joke and proclaimed the knight the winner.

Sir Tainwyn married the princess shortly afterwards, though sadly it wasn't a happy marriage. The dragon benefitted the most from the arrangement that they had made. What was his reward? He didn't have to work knight shifts ever again!

I can generate word families based on root words.
Page 45

(Answers may vary.)

port	import	important
believe	disbelieve	unbelievable
danger	dangerous	endangered
differ	different	indifference
appear	disappear	disappearance
possible	impossible	possibly
fair	unfair	unfairly
excite	excitement	unexcited
thank	thankful	thankless
spell	misspell	misspelled
view	review	reviewed
imagine	imagined	imagination

Year 4 Grammar & Punctuation

Autumn Assessment   ANSWERS

Name .... Class .... Date ....

1 Rewrite this sentence and put in any missing **full stops**, **capital letters** and **commas**.

we practise netball on tuesday wednesday and thursday

We practise netball on Tuesday, Wednesday and Thursday.
....

(Award 2 marks for all 6 identified. Award 1 mark for 4 or 5 identified.)

2 marks

2 Add a **full stop**, **question mark** or **exclamation mark** at the end of these sentences.

Call an ambulance | **!** |

Did you hand out the newsletters | **?** |

I took the register to the office | **.** |

(Award 2 marks for 3 correct. Award 1 mark for 2 correct.)

2 marks

3 Underline the **conjunctions** in each of these sentences.

He used to be a professional footballer <u>until</u> he injured his knee.

She used to have lots of friends <u>before</u> she moved to the new school.

(Award 2 marks for both correct.)

2 marks

4 Circle the **preposition** in the list below.

it   mine   (through)   because   grammar

(Award 1 mark for correct answer.)

1 mark

1

Page Total

Year 4 Grammar & Punctuation

5 Choose words to show that the order of the sentences below is correct. You can use a combination of **conjunctions**, **prepositions** and **adverbs** to express time. (The first one has been done for you.)

First .... he put the tea bag in the mug and boiled the water.

Next .... he poured the boiling water in the mug.

When .... the tea had brewed he took out the tea bag.

Finally .... he added milk and sugar to taste.

(Award 2 marks for 3 appropriate choices. Award 1 mark at teacher's discretion. Answers may vary.)

2 marks

6 Use the **possessive pronouns** in the box to complete the sentences below.

yours	mine	theirs

Arthur took my pen even though he knew it was............... **mine**.

Zoe and Ayesha said that the cat was............... **theirs**.

I found this scarf on the playground. I think it is .... **yours**.

(Award 1 mark for all 3 correct.)

1 mark

7 The sentences below are written in the **present tense**. Write the **past tense** of the **verbs** on the dotted lines.

I give chocolates to my mum on her birthday.

gave
....

We sleep in our caravan.

slept
....

(Award 2 marks for 2 correct. Award 1 mark for 1 correct.)

2 marks

2

Page Total

Year 4 Grammar & Punctuation

Autumn Assessment   ANSWERS

---

8 Circle the correct form of the **verb**, so that it is written in **Standard English**.

She (was standing) / were standing outside the gate when the school bell rang.

They **was practising** / (were practising) for their class assembly all morning.

(Award 2 marks for both correct, 1 mark for 1 correct.)

2 marks

---

9 Correct the following sentences so that they are written in **Standard English**.

I done all my homework.

I **have done** all my homework (Accept: I **did** …)
....

I have wrote it twice.
I **have written** it twice. (Accept: I **wrote** …)
....

(Award 2 marks for 2 correct. Award 1 mark for 1 correct.)

2 marks

---

10 Put **speech marks** in the sentences below.

"Where have you been?" asked Mum.

"I have been worried," she added.

(Award 2 marks for both correct. Award 1 mark for 1 correct.)

2 marks

---

11 Rewrite the following, putting the speech at the end of the sentence.

"I have seen United play twice," said Naeem.

Naeem said, "I have seen United play twice."
....

(Award 1 mark if speech marks have been placed correctly.)

1 mark

---

12 Put a circle around the **adverbs** in these sentences.

The tortoise made its way (slowly) to the finishing line.

Sit down (quickly) and open your books.

She shouted (angrily) at the misbehaving children.

(Award 1 mark if all 3 are correctly identified.)

1 mark

3

Page Total

Year 4 Grammar & Punctuation

---

13 Place the two most appropriate **conjunctions** from the box in the sentences below.

before	although	until	so

I won't play on the PlayStation ....**until**........... I have finished my spelling homework.

Tahir hurt my feelings ....**although**...... he didn't mean to.

(Award 2 marks for 2 correct. Award 1 mark for 1 correct.)

2 marks

---

14 Replace the underlined **proper nouns** in the sentence below with appropriate **pronouns**. (The proper nouns have been underlined for you.)

Hana hid Henry's mobile phone in Hana's coat pocket.

She   **his**   **her**
....

(Award 2 marks for all 3 correct. Award 1 mark for 2 correct.)

2 marks

---

15 Complete the sentence using a verb of your own in the **past progressive tense**.

I ....**was reading**.............. my book when you called.

(suggestion only)

(Award 1 mark for correct tense formation.)

1 mark

End of Autumn Assessment

Page Total

TOTAL

/ 25

PERCENTAGE SCORE

%

Year 4 Grammar & Punctuation

Spring Assessment — ANSWERS

Name .... Class .... Date ....

1 Rewrite this sentence and put in any missing **full stops**, **capital letters** and **commas**.

ben joe and sam are running

Ben, Joe and Sam are running.

(Award 2 marks for all 5 identified. Award 1 mark for 3 or 4 identified.)

2 marks

2 Draw a line matching the **verb** to another **verb** with a similar meaning. (The first one has been done for you.)

run — dash
ask — enquire
shut — close
shout — bellow
come back — return

(Award 2 marks for all 4 correct. Award 1 mark for 2 or 3 correct.)

2 marks

3 Change the structure of the sentence below so that it starts with the underlined **conjunction**.

I laughed <u>when</u> she told a joke.

When she told a joke, I laughed.

(Award 2 marks if correct. Award 1 mark if the comma has been omitted.)

2 marks

4 Use **two adjectives** of your own to describe the nouns in each of these sentences.

The ......**little**...... ......**old**...... man struggled to get out of his chair.

He crawled unseen through the ......**long**...... ......**green**...... grass.

(suggestions only)

(Award up to 2 marks for appropriate adjectives. Award 1 mark if paired adjectives are not in the correct order.)

2 marks

1

Page Total

5 Complete the sentences below with **subordinate clauses** of your own, using different **subordinating conjunctions**.

The teacher awarded the boy a certificate ...**because he had been**

working hard.

The old lady hurt her leg **when she fell on the icy pavement**.

....

(suggestions only)

(Award up to 2 marks for suitable subordinate clauses using subordinating conjunctions. Award 1 mark at teacher's discretion.)

2 marks

6 Circle the noun below which is a **non-countable noun**.

table   pencil   (bravery)   February

(Award 1 mark for a correct answer.)

1 mark

7 Choose the most appropriate **conjunctions** from the box below to complete the sentences.

before	so	although	while

Max pretended that he was in Year Three ....**so**........... that he would get into dinner first.

Mrs Jones managed to mark the books ....**while**........... the children were quietly working.

(Award 2 marks for 2 correct. Award 1 mark for 1 correct.)

2 marks

8 Complete the sentences by writing your own **prepositions** in the spaces.

Megan dropped the calculator ....**under**........... the table when she saw the teacher coming.

Charlie hid the answers to the tables test ....**between**........... two pieces of paper.

(Answers may vary. Award 2 marks for both appropriate prepositions. Award 1 mark for 1 appropriate preposition.)

2 marks

2

Page Total

Year 4 Grammar & Punctuation

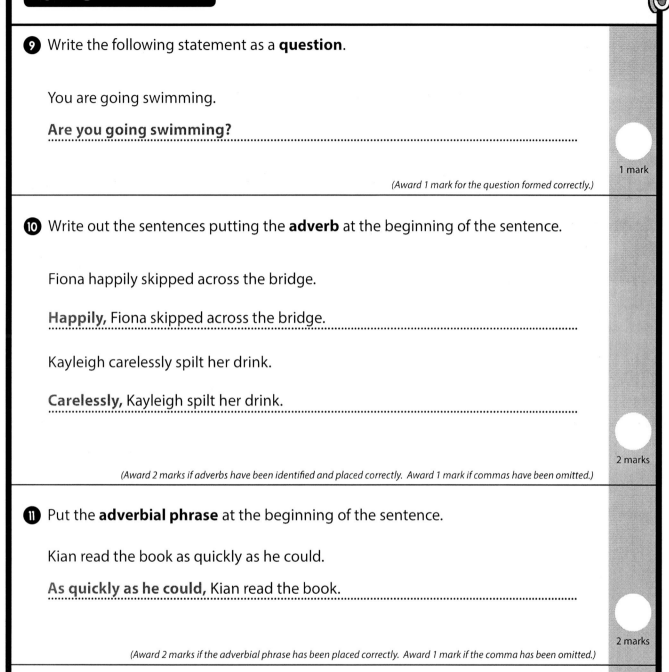

9 Write the following statement as a **question**.

You are going swimming.

Are you going swimming?

(Award 1 mark for the question formed correctly.)

1 mark

10 Write out the sentences putting the **adverb** at the beginning of the sentence.

Fiona happily skipped across the bridge.

Happily, Fiona skipped across the bridge.

Kayleigh carelessly spilt her drink.

Carelessly, Kayleigh spilt her drink.

(Award 2 marks if adverbs have been identified and placed correctly. Award 1 mark if commas have been omitted.)

2 marks

11 Put the **adverbial phrase** at the beginning of the sentence.

Kian read the book as quickly as he could.

As quickly as he could, Kian read the book.

(Award 2 marks if the adverbial phrase has been placed correctly. Award 1 mark if the comma has been omitted.)

2 marks

12 Underline the **adverbs** in these sentences.

George can run <u>fast</u>.

The teacher praises us <u>often</u>.

Tanya <u>always</u> ends up in trouble even when it isn't her fault.

(Award 1 mark if all 3 are correctly identified.)

1 mark

3

Page Total

Year 4 Grammar & Punctuation

---

13 Complete the sentences below with an appropriate **subordinate clause**.

Sienna liked the teacher who ....**who was kind to her**.............

....

Imran picked up the pencils which ....**had fallen onto the floor**............

....

(suggestions only)

(Award 2 marks for both subordinate clauses correctly completed. Award 1 mark at teacher's discretion.)

2 marks

---

14 Underline the **noun phrases** in these sentences.

<u>The derelict house with the broken windows</u> looked very scary.

<u>The boy in the striped red shirt</u> was very loud.

(Award 2 marks for 2 correct. Award 1 mark for 1 correct.)

2 marks

End of Spring Assessment

Page Total

TOTAL

25

PERCENTAGE SCORE

%

4

Year 4 Grammar & Punctuation

Summer Assessment ANSWERS

Name .... Class .... Date ....

---

1 Identify the different **word classes** (parts of speech) by putting the following words under the correct headings.

window	sadly	above	walked	because	she	massive

noun	verb	adjective	adverb
window	walked	massive	sadly

preposition	pronoun	conjunction
above	she	because

(Award 2 marks for all 7 correct. Award 1 mark for 5 or 6 correct.)

2 marks

---

2 Draw a line matching the **adjectives** to another **adjective** with a similar meaning. (The first one has been done for you.)

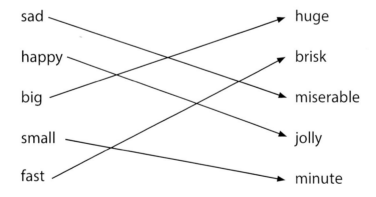

sad — miserable
happy — jolly
big — huge
small — minute
fast — brisk

(Award 2 marks for all 4 correct. Award 1 mark for 2 or 3 correct.)

2 marks

---

3 Circle the correct form of the **present perfect tense** to complete the sentence.

have thought / **have thinked** about nothing else.

(Award 1 mark for the correct form of the tense.)

1 mark

1

Page Total

Year 4 Grammar & Punctuation

Summer Assessment ANSWERS

4 Are the underlined clauses **coordinating clauses** or **subordinating clauses**? Circle the correct option.

She couldn't find her purse <u>although she had looked everywhere</u>.

coordinating (subordinate)

Tom leapt up from his chair, <u>and ran out of the classroom</u>.

(coordinating) / subordinate

(Award 2 marks for both correct. Award 1 mark for 1 correct.)

2 marks

5 Circle the correct **prefix** for each of the words below.

(un) / dis happy   (im) / un possible   (dis) / un agree

(Award 2 marks for all 3 correct. Award 1 mark for 2 correct.)

2 marks

6 Show you can use the **apostrophe for contraction** by writing the shorter version of these words.

do not ......**don't**......   I have ......**I've**......   he will ......**he'll**......

(Award 2 marks for all 3 correct. Award 1 mark for 2 correct.)

2 marks

7 Write the **irregular plural** of these nouns.

foot ......**feet**......   child ......**children**......   mouse ......**mice**......

(Award 1 mark for all 3 correct.)

1 mark

8 Underline the **subordinate clauses** in the following sentences.

Sam is drinking a glass of water <u>because she is thirsty</u>.

The children go into school <u>when the bell rings</u>.

(Award 2 marks for both correct. Award 1 mark for 1 correct.)

2 marks

Page Total

Year 4 Grammar & Punctuation

9 Rewrite the following phrases using the **apostrophe for possession**.

The pen of the headteacher ___the headteacher's pen___

The books of the children ___the children's books___

The cars of the teachers ___the teachers' cars___

2 marks

(Award 2 marks for 3 correct. Award 1 mark for 2 correct.)

10 Add the suffixes 'er' or 'est' to the adjectives in the brackets to complete the sentences.

You are **shorter** than your brother.

This is the **earliest** I have ever been up.

2 marks

(Award 2 marks for 2 correct. Award 1 mark for 1 correct.)

11 Add a **suffix** to these words so that the sentences make sense.

There was great **excitement** on the day of the school party.

He was extremely **thankful** that the term was nearly over.

2 marks

(Award 2 marks for both correct. Award 1 mark for 1 correct.)

12 Tick the **two** sentences where the **apostrophe** has been used correctly.

You're cat is in my house. ☐

My dog's paw is sore. ☑

It's time for your supper. ☑

I love your new roller skate's. ☐

2 marks

(Award 2 marks for both correct. Award 1 mark for 1 correct.)

Page Total

Year 4 Grammar & Punctuation

13 Circle the correct form of the **present perfect tense** in the sentences below.

I **have eaten** / **have ate** all the cabbage on my plate.

Ibrahim **is finished** / **has finished** the test.

2 marks

(Award 2 marks for 2 correct. Award 1 mark for 1 correct.)

14 Rewrite the sentence below with the correct **punctuation**.

I cant go to my friends house

I can't go to my friend's house.

1 mark

(Award 1 mark if all 3 are identified.)

End of Summer Assessment

Page Total

TOTAL

25

PERCENTAGE SCORE

%

4

Year 4 Grammar & Punctuation

Optional Test 1 ANSWERS

Name .... Class .... Date ....

1 Rewrite these sentences putting in any missing **punctuation** including **capital letters**.

mrs khan takes the class on a friday

Mrs Khan takes the class on a Friday.

have you read any roald dahl books

Have you read any Roald Dahl books?

(Award 3 marks for all 8 identified. Award 2 marks for 6 or 7 identified. Award 1 mark for 4 or 5 identified.)

3 marks

2 Complete the sentences with the most appropriate **conjunctions** from the box.

but	so	or	and

Would you like coffee .... **or** .... would you prefer tea?

She tried to get tickets for the match .... **but** ....they were sold out.

Jude wasn't feeling well .... **so** .... he stayed in bed.

(Award 2 marks for 3 correct. Award 1 mark for 2 correct.)

2 marks

3 Add a **full stop**, **question mark** or **exclamation mark** at the end of these sentences.

What a lovely surprise [**!**]

This book is very interesting [**.**]

Have you got any pets [**?**]

(Award 2 marks for 3 correct. Award 1 mark for 2 correct.)

2 marks

1

Page Total

Year 4 Grammar & Punctuation

Optional Test 1 ANSWERS

4 Use the **prepositions** in the box to complete the sentences below.

inside	through	across

The dog was sleeping **inside** its kennel.

He had to climb **through** the window to get in the house.

We walked **across** the wooden bridge.

(Award 2 marks for 3 correct. Award 1 mark for 2 correct.)

2 marks

5 Choose words to show that the order of the sentences below is correct. You can use a combination of **conjunctions**, **prepositions** and **adverbs** to express time. (The first one has been done for you.)

First .... she put the toothpaste on her toothbrush.

Next .... she turned on the tap and began brushing her teeth.

When .... her teeth were thoroughly clean, she rinsed out her mouth.

Finally .... she turned off the tap and smiled into the mirror.

(Award 2 marks if all words are appropriate. Award 1 mark at teacher's discretion. Answers may vary.)

2 marks

6 Add an appropriate **pronoun** in the space provided. (The first one has been done for you.)

These felt-tips belong to <u>us</u>. They are **ours**.

<u>The children</u> walked in single file. **They** were very well behaved.

That is <u>Eva's</u> magazine. It is **hers**.

The teacher told off <u>Henry and Habeeb</u>. He was very cross with **them**.

(Award 2 marks for 3 correct. Award 1 mark for 2 correct.)

2 marks

2

Page Total

Year 4 Grammar & Punctuation

7 Rewrite the **verbs** in the sentences below in the **past tense**. (Just write the verbs.)

The visitor speaks to the children in assembly.

spoke
....

He reads every night for a week.

read
....

I think about giving my pocket money to charity.

thought
....

(Award 1 mark for each correctly formed past tense verb.)

3 marks

8 Circle the correct form of the **progressive tense** in the sentences below.

I **walk** / (**am walking**) to school with my best friend.

She (**was collecting**) / **collected** all the exercise books at the end of the lesson.

(Award 2 marks for both correct. Award 1 mark for 1 correct.)

2 marks

9 Correct the following sentences so that they are written in **Standard English**.

I have brung my swimming kit today.

I have brought my swimming kit today.
....

I done my detention yesterday.

I did my detention yesterday.
....

(Award 1 mark for each correctly formed sentence.)

2 marks

Page Total

Year 4 Grammar & Punctuation

Optional Test 1 ANSWERS

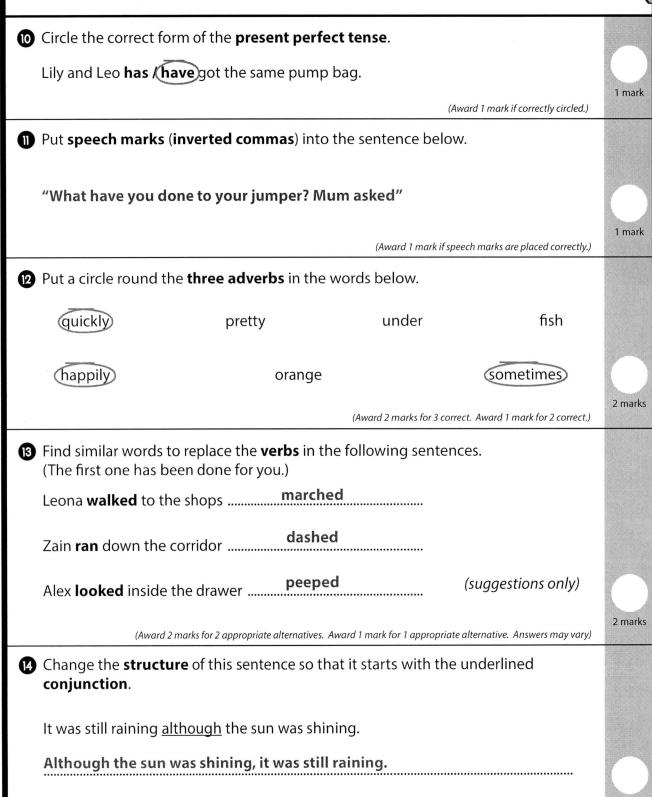

10 Circle the correct form of the **present perfect tense**.

Lily and Leo **has / have** got the same pump bag.

(Award 1 mark if correctly circled.)

1 mark

11 Put **speech marks** (**inverted commas**) into the sentence below.

"What have you done to your jumper? Mum asked"

(Award 1 mark if speech marks are placed correctly.)

1 mark

12 Put a circle round the **three adverbs** in the words below.

quickly   pretty   under   fish

happily   orange   sometimes

(Award 2 marks for 3 correct. Award 1 mark for 2 correct.)

2 marks

13 Find similar words to replace the **verbs** in the following sentences.
(The first one has been done for you.)

Leona **walked** to the shops ....**marched**............

Zain **ran** down the corridor ....**dashed**............

Alex **looked** inside the drawer ....**peeped**............   *(suggestions only)*

(Award 2 marks for 2 appropriate alternatives. Award 1 mark for 1 appropriate alternative. Answers may vary)

2 marks

14 Change the **structure** of this sentence so that it starts with the underlined **conjunction**.

It was still raining <u>although</u> the sun was shining.

Although the sun was shining, it was still raining.

(Award 2 marks if correctly restructured with appropriate punctuation. Award 1 mark if the comma has been omitted.)

2 marks

4

Page Total

Year 4 Grammar & Punctuation

15 Choose **two** appropriate **adjectives** from the list below to describe the nouns in the sentences.

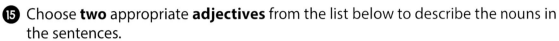

metal	furry	small	old

The .... *small furry* .... kitten was so cute.

The .... *old metal* .... gate was starting to rust.

(Award 1 mark if adjectives have been selected appropriately.)

1 mark

---

16 Complete the sentence below with an appropriate **subordinate clause**.

This is the girl who **rescued the cat**.

(suggestion only)

(Award 1 mark for any appropriate subordinate clause.)

1 mark

---

17 Extend the sentence below with a **noun phrase** to describe the alien.

The spaceman saw a green alien with **two heads**.

(suggestion only)

(Award 1 mark for an appropriate noun phrase.)

1 mark

---

18 Underline the **determiner** in the sentence below.

Josh watched **<u>an</u>** eagle swoop down.

(Award 1 mark for the determiner underlined.)

1 mark

5

Page Total

Year 4 Grammar & Punctuation

Optional Test 1 ANSWERS

19 Join the beginning and the end of each sentence with the correct **conjunction**. (The first one has been done for you.)

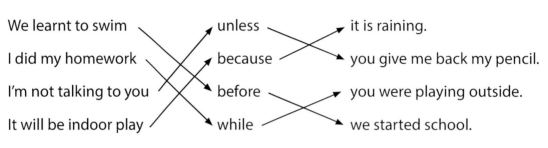

We learnt to swim — unless — it is raining.

I did my homework — because — you give me back my pencil.

I'm not talking to you — before — you were playing outside.

It will be indoor play — while — we started school.

(Award 2 marks for all 6 correctly matched lines. Award 1 mark at teacher's discretion.)

2 marks

20 Rewrite the sentence placing the **adverbial phrase** at the beginning.

She delivered the message as quickly as possible.

As quickly as possible, she delivered the message.

(Award 1 mark if the adverbial phrase has been placed at the beginning of the sentence using a comma.)

1 mark

21 Identify the different **word classes** (parts of speech) by putting the following words under the correct headings.

| inside | pencil | because | quietly | their | hid | strong |

noun	**verb**	**adjective**	**adverb**
pencil	hid	strong	quietly

preposition	**pronoun**	**conjunction**
inside	their	because

(Award 2 marks for all 7 correct. Award 1 mark for 5 or 6 correct.)

2 marks

22 Are the underlined clauses **coordinating clauses** or **subordinate clauses**? Circle the correct option.

The postman bit the dog <u>which had been barking</u>.

coordinating / (subordinate)

I've had my hair cut, <u>but I don't like the new style</u>.

(coordinating) / subordinate

(Award 2 marks for both correct. Award 1 mark for 1 correct.)

2 marks

6

Page Total

Year 4 Grammar & Punctuation

Optional Test 1 ANSWERS

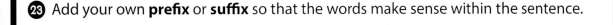

---

23 Add your own **prefix** or **suffix** so that the words make sense within the sentence.

Shana thought it was very **<u>un</u>fair** that she had never been chosen for the school netball team.

Our new sofa is so **comfor<u>table</u>** everyone wants to sit on it.

(Award 2 marks for both correct. Award 1 mark for 1 correct.)

2 marks

---

24 Rewrite the underlined words using the **apostrophe for contraction**.

I <u>have not</u> been to school today because <u>I have</u> not been feeling well. I <u>will not</u> be going to school tomorrow either.

haven't	**I've**	**won't**
....	....	....

(Award 2 marks for 3 correct. Award 1 mark for 2 correct.)

2 marks

---

25 Write the **plural** form of each of the following **nouns**.

brush   **brushes**   toy   **toys**

baby   **babies**   tooth   **teeth**

(Award 2 marks for 4 correctly spelt plurals. Award 1 mark for 2 or 3 correctly spelt plurals.)

2 marks

---

26 Underline the **subordinate clause** in the sentence below.

The car raced off <u>when the lights turned green</u>.

(Award 1 mark if the subordinate clause is correctly underlined.)

1 mark

7

Optional Test 1 ANSWERS

27 Write each phrase using the correct **apostrophe for possession**.
(The first one has been done for you.)

the dresses of the girls   the girls' dresses

the handbag of the lady   the lady's handbag

the prizes of the children   the children's prizes

the car of the teacher   the teacher's car

2 marks

(Award 2 marks for 3 correct. Award 1 mark for 2 correct.)

28 Add **prefixes** or **suffixes** to make **three** new words that belong to the same **word family**.

friend   friendly   unfriendly

     friendlier   *(suggestions only)*

2 marks

(Award 2 marks for all 3 correct. Award 1 mark for 2 correct.)

End of Optional Test 1

Page Total ◯

TOTAL

/ 50

PERCENTAGE SCORE

%

Year 4 Grammar & Punctuation

Optional Test 2 ANSWERS

Name .... Class .... Date ....

1 Rewrite these sentences putting in any missing **punctuation** including **capital letters**.

have you been to spain or france for your holidays

Have you been to Spain or France for your holidays?

we went to australia for all of august

We went to Australia for all of August.

3 marks

(Award 3 marks for all 8 identified. Award 2 marks for 6 or 7 identified. Award 1 mark for 4 or 5 identified.)

2 Complete the sentences with the most appropriate **conjunctions** from the box.

but	so	or	and

Should I sell my old video games ....**or**........... should I keep them?

We didn't want to miss the bus ....**so**...............we left the house in plenty of time.

Ava wanted to join the group ....**but**.............. the boys wouldn't let her.

2 marks

(Award 2 marks for 3 correct. Award 1 mark for 2 correct.)

3 Add a **full stop**, **question mark** or **exclamation mark** at the end of these sentences.

Get off my foot ⟨ **!** ⟩

When do you finish work ⟨ **?** ⟩

I would like to hear more of your story ⟨ **.** ⟩

2 marks

(Award 2 marks for 3 correct. Award 1 mark for 2 correct.)

1

Page Total

Year 4 Grammar & Punctuation

Optional Test 2 ANSWERS

---

4 Use the **prepositions** in the box to complete the sentences below.

over	along	after

The cat was creeping **along** the fence.

He had to climb **over** the wall to get into the garden.

We left school **after** our drama lesson.

(Award 2 marks for 3 correct. Award 1 mark for 2 correct.)

2 marks

---

5 Choose words to show that the order of the sentences below is correct. You can use a combination of **conjunctions**, **prepositions** and **adverbs** to express time. (The first one has been done for you.)

First .... put the dirty dishes in the dishwasher.

Next .... put in a dishwasher tablet and switch on the dishwasher.

When .... the dishwasher bleeps, the dishes will be clean.

Finally .... open the dishwasher door and put the clean dishes away.

(Award 2 marks if all words are appropriate. Award 1 mark at teacher's discretion. Answers may vary.)

2 marks

---

6 Add an appropriate **pronoun** in the space provided. (The first one has been done for you.)

This pencil case is <u>Jake's</u>. It is **his**.

Do you want <u>your</u> bag back? It is **yours**.

<u>Maria</u> doesn't want to talk to you. **She** doesn't want to be your friend.

<u>I</u> have had that pencil sharpener all year. It is **mine**.

(Award 2 marks for 3 correct. Award 1 mark for 2 correct.)

2 marks

2

Page Total

Year 4 Grammar & Punctuation

7 Rewrite the **verbs** in the sentences below in the **past tense**. (Just write the verbs.)

She catches the ball very well.

caught
....

She throws the sweet wrapper in the bin.

threw
....

The bird flies down from the tree.

flew
....

3 marks

(Award 1 mark for each correctly formed past tense verb.)

8 Circle the correct form of the **progressive tense** in the sentences below.

The boys **help** / ⟨**are helping**⟩ to clean up.

They ⟨**were skipping**⟩ / **skipped** on the playground.

2 marks

(Award 2 marks for both correct. Award 1 mark for 1 correct.)

9 Correct the following sentences so that they are written in **Standard English**.

She should of gone to the party.

She should have gone to the party.
....

I'm not going nowhere.

I'm not going anywhere. *(Accept: I'm going nowhere.)*
....

2 marks

(Award 1 mark for each correctly formed sentence.)

Page Total

Year 4 Grammar & Punctuation

Optional Test 2 ANSWERS

10 Circle the correct form of the **present perfect tense**.

Alex **has** / **have** got a lot of superhero figures.

(Award 1 mark if correctly circled.)

1 mark

11 Put **speech marks** (**inverted commas**) into the sentence below.

"Where should I hang my coat?" Finley asked.

(Award 1 mark if speech marks are placed correctly.)

1 mark

12 Put a circle round the **three adverbs** in the words below.

bad   silently   between   suddenly

fancy   always   wicked

(Award 2 marks for 3 correct. Award 1 mark for 2 correct.)

2 marks

13 Find similar words to replace the **verbs** in the following sentences.
(The first one has been done for you.)

The squirrel <u>ran</u> across the lawn.   darted

Jermaine <u>closed</u> the door.   shut

The cat <u>jumped</u> over the wall   leapt   *(suggestions only)*

(Award 2 marks for 2 appropriate alternatives. Award 1 mark for 1 appropriate alternative. Answers may vary)

2 marks

14 Change the **structure** of this sentence so that it starts with the underlined **conjunction**.

I won't give you a biscuit <u>unless</u> you ask nicely.

Unless you ask nicely, I won't give you a biscuit.

(Award 2 marks if correctly restructured with appropriate punctuation. Award 1 mark if the comma has been omitted.)

2 marks

4

Page Total

Year 4 Grammar & Punctuation

---

15 Choose **two** appropriate **adjectives** from the list below to describe the nouns in the sentences.

gold	round	small	shiny

The ....**shiny gold**........ ring was just what she wanted.

He threw the ....**small round**........ ball.

(Award 1 mark if adjectives have been selected appropriately.)

1 mark

---

16 Complete the sentence below with an appropriate **subordinate clause**.

That's the dog which **got into the school**.

(*suggestion only*)

(Award 1 mark for any appropriate subordinate clause.)

1 mark

---

17 Extend the sentence below with a **noun phrase** to describe the girl.

I spoke to the little girl with **the curly hair**.

(*suggestion only*)

(Award 1 mark for an appropriate noun phrase.)

1 mark

---

18 Underline the **determiner** in the sentence below.

Do <u>those</u> shoes belong to you?

(Award 1 mark for the determiner underlined.)

1 mark

5

Page Total

Year 4 Grammar & Punctuation

Optional Test 2 ANSWERS

19 Join the beginning and the end of each sentence with the correct **conjunction**.
(The first one has been done for you.)

You're not allowed on the PlayStation — while — you start behaving yourself.

We always do a maths test — until — you helped me.

I'll vacuum the carpet — because — you mop the kitchen floor.

I'll help you with your homework — before — we go out for morning play.

2 marks

(Award 2 marks for all 6 correctly matched lines. Award 1 mark at teacher's discretion.)

20 Rewrite the sentence placing the **adverbial phrase** at the beginning.

He got out of bed at the crack of dawn.

At the crack of dawn, he got out of bed.

1 mark

(Award 1 mark if the adverbial phrase has been placed at the beginning of the sentence using a comma.)

21 Identify the different **word classes** (parts of speech) by putting the following words under the correct headings.

loudly	under	knocked	they	yellow	although	door

noun	**verb**	**adjective**	**adverb**
door	knocked	yellow	loudly

preposition	**pronoun**	**conjunction**
under	they	although

2 marks

(Award 2 marks for all 7 correct. Award 1 mark for 5 or 6 correct.)

22 Are the underlined clauses **coordinating clauses** or **subordinate clauses**?
Circle the correct option.

I went on holiday with a suitcase <u>which weighed 24 kg</u>.

coordinating (subordinate)

My teacher gave me a sticker, <u>but I didn't really deserve it</u>.

(coordinating) subordinate

2 marks

(Award 2 marks for both correct. Award 1 mark for 1 correct.)

6

Page Total

Year 4 Grammar & Punctuation

23 Add your own **prefix** or **suffix** so that the words make sense within the sentence.

Bartek thought the mathematics problem was <u>**im**</u>**possible** to solve.

Please be **care**<u>**ful**</u> as you carry that hot cup of tea.

2 marks

(Award 2 marks for both correct. Award 1 mark for 1 correct.)

24 Rewrite the underlined words using the **apostrophe for contraction**.

<u>You are</u> not hungry, are you? <u>You will</u> have to wait because Mum <u>is not</u> home yet.

You're   **You'll**   **isn't**
....

2 marks

(Award 2 marks for 3 correct. Award 1 mark for 2 correct.)

25 Write the **plural** form of each of the following **nouns**.

box   **boxes**   person   **people**
....

leaf   **leaves**   table   **tables**
....

2 marks

(Award 2 marks for 4 correctly spelt plurals. Award 1 mark for 2 or 3 correctly spelt plurals.)

26 Underline the **subordinate clause** in the sentence below.

He went outside to play <u>after he had finished his tea</u>.

1 mark

(Award 1 mark if the subordinate clause is correctly underlined.)

7

Page Total

© Copyright HeadStart Primary Ltd

Year 4 Grammar & Punctuation

Optional Test 2 ANSWERS

27 Write each phrase using the correct **apostrophe for possession**.
(The first one has been done for you.)

the gloves of the girl .... **the girl's gloves** ....

the pictures of the artists .... **the artists' pictures** ....

the shoes of the men .... **the men's shoes** ....

the tail of the dog .... **the dog's tail** ....

2 marks

(Award 2 marks for 3 correct. Award 1 mark for 2 correct.)

28 Add **prefixes** or **suffixes** to make **three** new words that belong to the same **word family**.

excite .... **exciting** .... **unexciting** ....

.... **excitedly** .... *(suggestions only)*

2 marks

(Award 2 marks for all correct. Award 1 mark for 2 correct.)

End of Optional Test 2

Page Total

TOTAL

/ 50

PERCENTAGE SCORE

%

Year 4 Grammar & Punctuation

Optional Test 3 ANSWERS

Name .... Class .... Date ....

1 Rewrite these sentences putting in any missing **punctuation** including **capital letters**.

The train for london departs every tuesday

The train for London departs every Tuesday.
....

will it be stopping at wigan and crewe

Will it be stopping at Wigan and Crewe?
....

3 marks

(Award 3 marks for all 8 identified. Award 2 marks for 6 or 7 identified. Award 1 mark for 4 or 5 identified.)

2 Complete the sentences with the most appropriate **conjunctions** from the box.

but	so	or	and

Anna wanted to go to the party ....**but**.......... her dad said she couldn't go.

I might play out with Harry ....**or**.......... I might just stay at home.

I really wanted the pizza ....**so**.......... I pushed to the front of the queue.

2 marks

(Award 2 marks for 3 correct. Award 1 mark for 2 correct.)

3 Add a **full stop**, **question mark** or **exclamation mark** at the end of these sentences.

I'll have a biscuit, please [**.**]

Why are you doing that [**?**]

That hurts [**!**]

2 marks

(Award 2 marks for 3 correct. Award 1 mark for 2 correct.)

1

Page Total

Year 4 Grammar & Punctuation

4 Use the **prepositions** in the box to complete the sentences below.

before	behind	during

Javed was hiding **behind** the curtain.

Rhiannon talked non-stop **during** the maths lesson.

We washed our hands **before** we went in to dinner.

(Award 2 marks for 3 correct, 1 mark for 2 correct.)

2 marks

5 Choose words to show that the order of the sentences below is correct. You can use a combination of **conjunctions**, **prepositions** and **adverbs** to express time. (The first one has been done for you.)

First........ put the plug in the plughole and fill the bath with hot water.

Next........ mix with cold water until it is the right temperature.

When........ the water is the right depth, turn off the taps.

Finally........ enjoy a relaxing bath.

(Award 2 marks if all words are appropriate. Award 1 mark at teacher's discretion. Answers may vary.)

2 marks

6 Add an appropriate **pronoun** in the space provided. (The first one has been done for you.)

That ball belongs to <u>Frankie and Bernie</u>. It is **theirs**.

I've got your <u>diary</u>. Do you want **it** back?

That belongs to <u>Fern and me</u>. It is **ours**.

Hello, <u>Toby</u>. How are **you**?

(Award 2 marks for 3 correct. Award 1 mark for 2 correct.)

2 marks

2

Page Total

Year 4 Grammar & Punctuation

Optional Test 3 ANSWERS

7 Rewrite the **verbs** in the sentences below in the **past tense**. (Just write the verbs.)

The robber steals a ring from the jewellery shop.

stole
....

I go to the park with my older brother.

went
....

The teacher teaches us some French words.

taught
....

(Award 1 mark for each correctly formed past tense verb.)

3 marks

8 Circle the correct form of the **progressive tense** in the sentences below.

The dog **chases** (**is chasing**) the cat.

The children (**were following**) **followed** the teacher.

(Award 2 marks for both correct. Award 1 mark for 1 correct.)

2 marks

9 Correct the following sentences so that they are written in **Standard English**.

They does everything wrong.

They <u>do</u> everything wrong.
....

It were a silly thing to do!

It <u>was</u> a silly thing to do!
....

(Award 1 mark for each correctly formed sentence.)

2 marks

Page Total

Year 4 Grammar & Punctuation

Optional Test 3 ANSWERS

---

10 Circle the correct form of the **present perfect tense**.

Ricky and Daniel **has / (have)** worked hard all day.

(Award 1 mark if correctly circled.)

1 mark

---

11 Put **speech marks (inverted commas)** into the sentence below.

"Will you go with me to the school office?" Polina asked.

(Award 1 mark if speech marks are placed correctly.)

1 mark

---

12 Put a circle round the **three adverbs** in the words below.

(bravely)   honest   cheese

because   above   (politely)   (often)

(Award 2 marks for 3 correct. Award 1 mark for 2 correct.)

2 marks

---

13 Find similar words to replace the **verbs** in the following sentences.
(The first one has been done for you.)

Charlotte <u>laughed</u> at the teacher's joke. **chuckled** ....

Arun <u>ran</u> very fast. **sprinted** ....

Adam <u>bellowed</u> at the top of his voice. **shouted** ....   *(suggestions only)*

(Award 2 marks for 2 appropriate alternatives. Award 1 mark for 1 appropriate alternative. Answers may vary.)

2 marks

---

14 Change the **structure** of this sentence so that it starts with the underlined **conjunction**.

You can't have your phone back <u>until</u> you say sorry.

Until you say sorry, you can't have your phone back.

(Award 2 marks if correctly restructured with appropriate punctuation. Award 1 mark if the comma has been omitted.)

2 marks

Page Total

Year 4 Grammar & Punctuation

Optional Test 3 ANSWERS

---

15 Choose **two** appropriate **adjectives** from the list below to describe the nouns in the sentences.

young	wooden	handsome	green

The ...... *green wooden* ...... door slowly creaked open.

The ...... *handsome young* ...... man showed me to my seat.

(Award 1 mark if adjectives have been selected appropriately.)

1 mark

---

16 Complete the sentence below with an appropriate **subordinate clause**.

This is the book that **we read in class**.

(suggestion only)

(Award 1 mark for any appropriate subordinate clause.)

1 mark

---

17 Extend the sentence below with a **noun phrase** to describe the dog.

I stroked the big dog with **the floppy ears**.

(suggestion only)

(Award 1 mark for an appropriate noun phrase.)

1 mark

---

18 Underline the **determiner** in the sentence below.

I go there <u>every</u> day.

(Award 1 mark for the determiner underlined.)

1 mark

5

Page Total

Year 4 Grammar & Punctuation

19 Join the beginning and the end of each sentence with the correct **conjunction**. (The first one has been done for you.)

We went in the swimming pool   because   I have a go on the scooter.

You can have one of my sweets   after   you have been kind to me.

We're both in trouble   while   we had a shower.

You can wear my rollerblades   unless   you tell the truth.

(Award 2 marks for all 6 correctly matched lines. Award 1 mark at teacher's discretion.)

2 marks

20 Rewrite the sentence placing the **adverbial phrase** at the beginning.

I heard the bad news later that day.

Later that day, I heard the bad news.

(Award 1 mark if the adverbial phrase has been placed at the beginning of the sentence using a comma.)

1 mark

21 Identify the different **word classes** (parts of speech) by putting the following words under the correct headings.

favourite	above	quickly	ruler	whistled	because	her

noun	verb	adjective	adverb
ruler	whistled	favourite	quickly

preposition	pronoun	conjunction
above	her	because

(Award 2 marks for all 7 correct. Award 1 mark for 5 or 6 correct.)

2 marks

22 Are the underlined clauses **coordinating clauses** or **subordinate clauses**? Circle the correct option.

I ran all the way, <u>but I was still late for school</u>. (**coordinating**) / **subordinate**

I believed the story <u>which she told me at lunchtime</u>.

coordinating / (**subordinate**)

(Award 2 marks for both correct. Award 1 mark for 1 correct.)

2 marks

6

Page Total

Year 4 Grammar & Punctuation

23 Add your own **prefix** or **suffix** so that the words make sense within the sentence.

Layla told me it was **dis<u>honest</u>** to take the money from the drawer.

Neha said that the puncture made her bicycle **use<u>less</u>**.

○ 2 marks

(Award 2 marks for both correct. Award 1 mark for 1 correct.)

24 Rewrite the underlined words using the **apostrophe for contraction**.

<u>Do not</u> go on the grass! <u>There is</u> a sign to say that you <u>must not</u> go on it.

Don't   **There's**   **mustn't**

○ 2 marks

(Award 2 marks for 3 correct. Award 1 mark for 2 correct.)

25 Write the **plural** form of each of the following **nouns**.

tree   **trees**   branch   **branches**

life   **lives**   sheep   **sheep**

○ 2 marks

(Award 2 marks for 4 correctly spelt plurals. Award 1 mark for 2 or 3 correctly spelt plurals.)

26 Underline the **subordinate clause** in the sentence below.

Year 3 went out to play <u>before the bell went</u>.

○ 1 mark

(Award 1 mark if the subordinate clause is correctly underlined.)

Page Total ○

Year 4 Grammar & Punctuation

27 Write each phrase using the correct **apostrophe for possession**.
(The first one has been done for you.)

the whiskers of the cat

> the cat's whiskers

the costumes of the actors

> the actors' costumes

the hats of the women

> the women's hats

the roar of the giant

> the giant's roar

2 marks

(Award 2 marks for 3 correct. Award 1 mark for 2 correct.)

28 Add **prefixes** or **suffixes** to make **three** new words that belong to the same **word family**.

agree

> disagree   agreement

> disagreement   *(suggestions only)*

2 marks

(Award 2 marks for all 3 correct. Award 1 mark for 2 correct.)

End of Optional Test 3

Page Total ◯

TOTAL

/ 50

PERCENTAGE SCORE

%

Assessments/Test Analysis

Record Sheets

Raw score/scaled score conversion charts for the Optional Tests are supplied on the CD-ROM.

Year 4

Children's Names

	Autumn			Spring			Summer			Optional 1			Optional 2			Optional 3		
	Raw score	%	Stage	Raw score	%	Stage	Raw score	%	Stage	Raw score	Scaled score	Stage	Raw score	Scaled score	Stage	Raw score	Scaled score	Stage

YEAR 4

ANALYSIS GRID

Question Objectives

	Total correct per question	Percentage per question
1. Full stops, capital letters, commas		
2. Full stops, question marks, exclamation marks		
3. Conjunctions		
4. Prepositions		
5. Words to express time		
6. Possessive pronouns		
7. Past tense		
8. Auxiliary verbs (Standard English)		
9. Standard English		
10. Speech marks		
11. Speech (at end of sentence)		
12. Adverbs		
13. Conjunctions		
14. Pronouns		
15. Past progressive		
Children's Scores		
Percentages		

Enlarge to A3 for added clarity

YEAR 4

ANALYSIS GRID

Children's Names

Question Objectives	Total correct per question	Percentage per question
1. Full stops, capital letters and commas		
2. Alternative verbs		
3. Conjunctions (identify)		
4. Paired adjectives		
5. Subordinate conjunctions / clauses		
6. Non-countable nouns		
7. Conjunctions		
8. Prepositions		
9. Questions		
10. Adverbs		
11. Fronted adverbial phrases		
12. Adverbs (that don't end in 'ly')		
13. Subordinate clauses		
14. Noun phrases		
Children's Scores		
Percentages		

YEAR 4

ANALYSIS GRID

Children's Names

Question Objectives

	Total correct per question	Percentage per question
1. Word classes (parts of speech)		
2. alternative adjectives		
3. Present perfect		
4. Co-ordinating clauses / subordinate clauses		
5. Prefixes		
6. Apostrophe for contraction		
7. Irregular plurals		
8. Subordinate clauses		
9. Apostrophe for possession		
10. Adjectives to compare		
11. Suffixes		
12. Apostrophe (correct usage)		
13. Present perfect		
14. Punctuation		
Children's Scores		
Percentages		

Enlarge to A3 for added clarity

Optional Tests   YEAR 4

ANALYSIS GRID

Please mark as **OPTIONAL 1 2** or **3**

Children's Names

Question Objectives	Total correct per question	Percentage per question
1. Punctuation – Capital letters, full stops, question marks		
2. Conjunctions (co-ordinating)		
3. Full stops, question marks, exclamation marks		
4. Prepositions		
5. Words to express time		
6. Pronouns		
7. Irregular past tense		
8. Progressive tense		
9. Standard English		
10. Present perfect		
11. Speech marks		
12. Adverbs		
13. Alternative verbs		
14. Sentence structure		
15. Paired adjectives		
16. Subordinate clauses		
17. Noun phrases		
18. Determiners		
19. Conjunctions (subordinating)		
20. Fronted adverbial phrases		
21. Word classes (parts of speech)		
22. Co-ordinating clauses / subordinate clauses		
23. Prefixes / suffixes		
24. Apostrophe for contraction		
25. Plurals		
26. Subordinate clause (identify)		
27. Apostrophe for possession		
28. Word families		
Raw Scores		
Scaled Scores		

NATIONAL CURRICULUM STATUTORY REQUIREMENTS

RECORD SHEET (YEARS 3 AND 4)

Children's Names

Pupils should be taught to develop their understanding of the concepts set out in English Appendix 2 by:

- extending the range of sentences with more than one clause by using a wider range of conjunctions
- using the present perfect form of verbs in contrast to the past tense
- choosing nouns or pronouns appropriately for clarity and cohesion and to avoid repetition
- using conjunctions, adverbs and prepositions to express time and cause
- using fronted adverbials
- learning the grammar for years 3 and 4 in English Appendix 2

Pupils should be taught to indicate grammatical and other features by:

- using commas after fronted adverbials
- indicating possession by using the possessive apostrophe with plural nouns
- using and punctuating direct speech

Pupils should be taught to use and understand the grammatical terminology in English Appendix 2 accurately and appropriately

Enlarge to A3 for added clarity

National Curriculum Coverage & Notes

National Curriculum Coverage and Notes

Teachers will note that, within the activity sheets, there are a number of exercises that consolidate previous learning, as well as exercises that go beyond the National Curriculum requirements for a particular age group. In the English Programme of Study (page 6 of the introduction) it states:

"Within each key stage, schools have the flexibility to introduce content earlier or later than set out in the programme of study. In addition, schools can introduce key stage content during an earlier key stage if appropriate."

At HeadStart, we believe that there are a number of appropriate concepts that can be introduced at an earlier stage than stated in English Appendix 2. For example, in the Year 3 and Year 4 Programme of Study for writing composition, it states that children need to build a 'varied and rich vocabulary' (page 29), yet the term 'synonym' is not introduced until Year 6 of Appendix 2 (page 69). We have, therefore, introduced the use of synonyms at a much earlier age, though children will not be tested on the knowledge of the term "synonym" until the appropriate key stage.

Coverage

The following tables show the year group when the concepts are first introduced in the Programme of Study, either in the Statutory Requirements or in the Appendix. Some concepts appear under Spelling or Writing and have been included because of their close relationship to grammar. Some concepts, e.g. irregular adjectives to compare (comparative and superlative), are not mentioned in the Statutory Requirements, but have been included because of the importance of teaching children Standard English. (For example, children need to understand not to use "more bigger", or "my bestest friend", or "worserer".)

Coverage - Book 1

Learning Objectives	National Curriculum Programme of Study		
	Statutory Requirements	**Appendix 2**	**Glossary/ Spelling/ Writing**
Chapter One			
1. Capital letters, full stops and commas	Year 2		
2. Conjunctions	Year 2, 3 & 4	Year 2 & 3	
3. Full stops, question marks, exclamation marks	Year 2		
4. Prepositions	Year 3 & 4	Year 3	
5. Words to express time	Year 3 & 4	Year 3	
6. Pronouns	Year 3 & 4	Year 4	Writing Y3 & 4
7. Present and past tense	Year 2, 3 & 4	Year 2	
8. Auxiliary verbs	Year 2	Year 2 & 3	
9. Direct speech	Year 3 & 4	Year 3	
10. Adverbs	Year 3 & 4	Year 2	
Chapter Two			
1. Alternative verbs			Writing Y3 & 4
2. Sentence structure			Writing Y3 & 4
3. Paired adjectives	Year 2		
4. Clauses within sentences	Year 5 & 6		Writing Y3 & 4
5. Non-countable nouns			Glossary
6. Linking ideas in sentences	Year 3 & 4		
7. Prepositions	Year 3 & 4	Year 3	
8. Statements into questions	Year 2	Year 2	
9. Fronted adverbials	Year 3 & 4	Year 4	
10. Adverbs (not ending in 'ly')	Year 3 & 4		Glossary
Chapter Three			
1. Word classes (parts of speech)	Year 3, 4, 5 & 6		Glossary
2. Alternative adjectives			Writing Y3 & 4
3. Present perfect and past perfect	Year 5 & 6	Year 3	
4. Different sentence structures	Year 2, 3 & 4	Year 2 & 3	
5. Prefixes		Year 3	Spelling Y1, 3 & 4
6. Apostrophe for contraction	Year 2	Year 2	
7. Regular and irregular plurals		Year 1	Spelling Y1
8. Determiners		Year 3 & 6	Writing Y3 & 4
9. Apostrophe for possession	Year 2, 3 & 4	Year 2 & 4	Spelling Y2, 3 & 4
10. Regular and irregular adjectives to compare (Standard English)		Year 2	Spelling Y 1 & 2

Coverage – Book 2

Learning Objectives	National Curriculum Programme of Study		
(Headings marked with the crossed swords symbol ✖ denote concepts not covered in Book 1.)	**Statutory Requirements**	**Appendix 2**	**Glossary/ Spelling/ Writing**
1. Capital letters, full stops and commas	Year 2		
2. Conjunctions	Year 2, 3 & 4	Year 2 & 3	
3. Full stops, question marks, exclamation marks	Year 2		
4. Prepositions	Year 3 & 4	Year 3	
5. Words to express time	Year 3 & 4	Year 3	
6. Pronouns	Year 3 & 4	Year 4	Writing Y2, 3 & 4
7. Present and past tense	Year 2, 3 & 4	Year 2	
8. **Progressive tense** ✖	Year 2	Year 2	Glossary
9. Auxiliary verbs	Year 2	Year 2 & 3	
10. **Standard English (1)** ✖		Year 4	Glossary
11. **Standard English (2)** ✖		Year 4	Glossary
12. **Standard English (3)** ✖		Year 4	Glossary
13. Direct speech	Year 3 & 4	Year 3	
14. **Direct / reported speech** ✖			Writing Y3 & 4
15. Adverbs	Year 3 & 4	Year 2	
16. Alternative verbs		Year 6	Writing Y3 & 4
17. Sentence structure			Writing Y3 & 4
18. Paired adjectives (1)	Year 2		
19. Paired adjectives (2)	Year 2		
20. Clauses within sentences	Year 5 & 6		Writing Y3 & 4
21. **Relative pronouns** ✖	Year 5 & 6	Year 5	Glossary
22. Countable and non-countable nouns			Glossary
23. **Noun phrases** ✖	Year 2, 5 & 6	Year 2 & 4	Glossary
24. Linking ideas in sentences	Year 3 & 4		
25. Prepositions	Year 3 & 4	Year 3	
26. Statements into questions	Year 2	Year 2	
27. Fronted adverbials	Year 3 & 4		
28. **Fronted adverbial phrases** ✖	Year 3 & 4	Year 4	Glossary
29. Adverbs (not ending in ly)	Year 3 & 4		Glossary
30. Word classes (parts of speech)	Year 3, 4, 5 & 6		Glossary
31. Alternative words		Year 6	Writing Y3 & 4
32. Present perfect and past perfect	Year 5 & 6	Year 3	
33. Different sentence structures	Year 2, 3 & 4	Year 2 & 3	
34. Prefixes		Year 3	Spelling Y1, 3 & 4
35. Apostrophe for contractions	Year 2	Year 2	
36. Regular and irregular plurals		Year 1	Spelling Y1
37. **Parts of a sentence** ✖		Year 3 & 6	Writing Y3 & 4
38. Apostrophe for possession	Year 2, 3 & 4	Year 3 & 6	Spelling Y2, 3 & 4
39. **Correct use of the apostrophe (1)** ✖		Year 4	Spelling Y2, 3 & 4
40. **Correct use of the apostrophe (2)** ✖			Spelling Y3 & 4
41. Regular and irregular adjectives to compare (Standard English) (1)		Year 2	Spelling Y1 & 2
42. Regular and irregular adjectives to compare (Standard English) (2)		Year 2	Spelling Y1 & 2
43. **Paragraphs (1)** ✖		Year 3 & 4	Writing Y3 & 4
44. **Paragraphs (2)** ✖		Year 3 & 4	Writing Y3 & 4
45. **Word families** ✖		Year 3	Glossary/Spelling

Coverage *(continued)*

The following table shows how the programmes of study are covered by the scheme of work presented in this book.

Pupils should be taught to:
develop their understanding of the concepts set out in English Appendix 2 by:

extending the range of sentences with more than one clause by using a wider range of conjunctions, including when, if, because, although			
Book 1	p 5 – 8, 45 – 48, 93 – 96	Book 2	p2, 33

using the present perfect form of verbs in contrast to the past tense			
Book 1	p 89 – 92	Book 2	p 32

choosing nouns or pronouns appropriately for clarity and cohesion and to avoid repetition			
Book 1	p 21 – 24	Book 2	p 6

using conjunctions, adverbs and prepositions to express time and cause			
Book 1	p17 – 20, 61 – 64	Book 2	p 5, 24

using fronted adverbials			
Book 1	p 73 – 76	Book 2	p 27, 28

learning the grammar for years 3 and 4 in English Appendix 2

Pupils should be taught to:
indicate grammatical and other features by:

using commas after fronted adverbials			
Book 1	p 73 – 76	Book 2	p 27, 28

indicating possession by using the possessive apostrophe with plural nouns			
Book 1	p 113 – 116	Book 2	p 38, 39

using and punctuating direct speech			
Book 1	p 33 – 36	Book 2	p 13, 14

Pupils should be taught to:
use and understand the grammatical terminology in English Appendix 2 accurately and appropriately when discussing their reading and writing.

Appendix 2: Vocabulary, grammar and punctuation

The grammatical difference between plural and possessive –s			
Book 1	**p 113 – 116**	**Book 2**	**p 36, 38**

Standard English forms for verb inflections instead of local spoken forms			
		Book 2	**p 10, 11, 12**

Noun phrases expanded by the addition of modifying adjectives, nouns and preposition phrases			
		Book 2	**p 23, 28**

Fronted adverbials			
Book 1	**p 73 – 76**	**Book 2**	**p 28**

Use of paragraphs to organise ideas around a theme			
		Book 2	**p 43, 44**

Appropriate choice of pronoun or noun within and across sentences to aid cohesion and avoid repetition			
Book 1	**p 21 – 24**	**Book 2**	**p 6**

Use of inverted commas and other punctuation to indicate direct speech (for example, end punctuation with inverted commas)			
Book 1	**p 33 – 36**	**Book 2**	**p 13**

Apostrophes to mark plural possession			
Book 1	**p 113 – 116**	**Book 2**	**p 38, 39**

Use of commas after fronted adverbials			
Book 1	**p 73 – 76**	**Book 2**	**p 27, 28**